Coffee Shop University

A book about mythology, spirituality, philosophy, psychology, religion, politics, economics and the ecology...

Mario Kfoury

ISBN 978-0-9955679-0-0
British Library Cataloguing in Publication Data
A CIP catalogue record for this book can be obtained from the
British Library.

Book layout and cover design by Freyja.
Cover image © Rfischia | Dreamstime.com
The cover design copyrights are the property of the Author.
Typeset, printed and bound by CPI Group (UK) Ltd.

http://cometpublications.webs.com

Contents

Preface

If you caution people about what might happen in the next hours or days, never mind the next few decades, they will laugh in your face and reproach you with a grain of sarcasm for impersonating a prophet. Yet they believe in what was written thousands of years ago, maybe because time has cashed its dues and sunk them deep down into their subconscious, where they now belong to the realm of the inaccessible. It might also be perhaps that it does not constitute a direct threat or challenge anymore to their present opinion, creed or philosophy because they have become their actual and accepted creed and philosophy; and yet the law is all too clear.

According to Isaac Newton's Third Law of Motion, "*For every action there is an equal and opposite reaction*", and to Antoine Lavoisier's Law of Mass Conservation, "*Nothing new is created nor lost under the sun, but everything is transformed*". If you leave your house in the morning without attending to the small nuisance in your car, sooner or later it will fail on you, and you will have to call in the towing services and the mechanic. This trivial case reveals how much there is to that same law that reverberates across all spheres of life.

"*Whatever can go wrong, will go wrong*" observed Edward Murphy Jr, an American aerospace engineer who worked on safety critical systems. The corollaries are many, but the origin is always the same: the never-ending, never-bending wheel of life, the Universal Law of Karma.

My name is Mario and I am here to tell a story.

Part I

1. The Beginning

Bailey's Gym, Los Angeles, California — 6am — the fall of 1999. I was just finishing the last reps of a chest dumbbells fly exercise with a pair of medium weights when the waves of the FM station started broadcasting some strange lyrics. I interrupted my training to catch my breath, wiped off the sweat and listened. Sitting on the edge of the bench, I tried to comprehend what was being said. The words sounded like a song, yet I was sure it wasn't one.

Mesmerized by the rhythm and tempo, I focused to catch every word I could put my mind on. Could it be that the DJ was so wise as to discourse in such a way on that morning, or was it that I still hadn't fully awakened? Life is so well designed that sometimes, when we are at a critical crossroads ready and totally committed to our quest, providence intervenes to assist us in our sacred journey. Like the pieces of a puzzle, which bit by bit gather and take shape to complement the whole picture we have been trying to decipher and understand. Thank you, Baz Luhrmann, for the 'sunscreen' song. [1]

That same year *The Matrix* movie was released, and while some people watched the action scenes and special effects in awe, not apprehending its full depth and implications, others were seduced without knowing why by some subliminal imperceptible messages. Critics and commentators drew parallels to *Alice in Wonderland's* rabbit hole and Plato's *Myth of the Cave*, but Jean Baudrillard's book *Simulacra and Simulation* was much more distinct and visible in the movie, as it was on Neo's bedside table. I thought the movie was a masterpiece and went back many times to watch it, but one sentence in particular inadvertently caught my attention and kept visiting my brain, sparking my gray matter. It was Morpheus telling Neo, *"It's the question that drives us, Neo. It's the question that brought you here."* [2]

* * *

In 1975 the war broke out in Lebanon. I was a kid then and spent a lot of time pondering why men make war. Is it that we are so different, physiologically or psychologically? If so, where did that difference reside or come from? Would the Cold War turn into a hot one with the oppressive communist regimes, and would they ever use the atomic bomb in a desperate move of repression? So many fears, besides the ordinary ones of growing up, to add to the anxiety any human being under usual stress undergoes, especially when the marrow of his personality is still weak, vulnerable and morphing.

As children or later on teenagers, we all go through periods of rebellion in life against authority, politics, established paradigms — almost anything we can put our hands on to confront, break up with the previous stage, claim and consolidate our independence. But what drives us initially to that pursuit is usually something we feel, deep down in our guts, is bigger and more important than the objects of our agitation. It is the call for answers to the three eternal 'W's: "Where are we coming from?"; "What are we doing here?"; and "Where are we going to?"

It might also be that what I was doing there, at that particular place and time, was directly related to these questions. The irony of the matter was that some of the most interesting stories depicting those journeys almost all winded up at the vantage point of their respective beginning; but where to start and what to look for?

* * *

In 1987, right after school, at the height of the civil war, I made up my mind to sell my car, pack my bag and set sail to a place I'd always dreamed of: Los Angeles, CA, to meet my best buddy Elrob and work out together in the oldest and most legendary gyms in the world. Back then I had only a few dollars for my subsistence, but was devoted to becoming independent, experiencing the American dream and testing what they taught us at school about real life.

It was a very memorable time indeed, spent in a land of diversity, freedom and opportunity for the person capable of appreciating such possibilities. When one comes from a different culture, one's viewpoints are still immersed in a totally different mind-set, founded on well anchored static thoughts, ideas, opinions and beliefs confirmed by pre-established conceptions or misconceptions, all locked up in a well-secured and defended safety deposit box of values, rituals, traditions or superstitions. All this baggage shapes one's perceptions, in subtle or flagrant ways, breeding gaps and differences between the visitor and the hosting environment. After a while, the pairing and exchanging of data occurs and transformation kicks in — what's called in political lingo: 'integration or miss-integration, assimilation or alienation' depending on the compatibility or incompatibility of the CBOS (Core Beliefs Operating System) tied to a most essential level of free will, willingness and disposition. Everything in life is a process; it takes time, especially after a certain age, for new ideas and beliefs to sink in deep and settle, taking up residence, triggering synapses, forging new neuronal networks and pathways.

* * *

We were young and reckless at that time, eager to find a job, prove our worth and realize something in this world. We had big dreams and great expectations. Every morning after the gym, we would meet at the local coffee shop before heading to work. The waitress had an eye on Elrob as he was Junior Mr. World, but the guy was keen on his girlfriend.

We started as security officers for an exclusive beach resort, tried other trades, and after many trials and tribulations managed to get a bank loan and put some money down on a real estate deal, then rent out the place to pay off the mortgage. Our daily routine consisted of training, looking after the very special diet we believed was essential for a bodybuilder, working, then later at night more training. At the weekend we would do the laundry, go to the supermarket and run other errands. Life was simple and gratifying.

I was at that time still obsessed with war. Having started martial arts training a few years back in Beirut, I felt it was essential to study it from all perspectives. My bookshelves were filled with titles from Sun Tzu, Miyamoto Musashi, Yagyu Munenori, Carl von Clausewitz, to name a few, as well as all the available bodybuilding and martial arts books and magazines of that time. Every week we would race, Elrob and I, to the neighborhood's newsstand to be first to put our hands on the new publications, learn the latest training and nutrition secrets, test them and brag about them in the gym. Our fascination was in developing physical prowess to the maximum level. And we didn't miss an opportunity to show it off, sometimes even drawing immense pleasure from unveiling it in discreet ways, pretending it to be humbleness.

* * *

Once in Santa Monica, my neighbor Robert from across the street, a cameraman for a golf sports TV station, came to greet me as a newcomer on the block and started asking personal questions about my background which made me feel nervous. For when he discovered I was from the Middle East, he got suspicious and started taking pictures of me and my house, threatening to report me to the FBI as a terrorist. I wasn't in a good mood at that time so I pushed him to the door and asked him to leave as I was fulminating.

When I told Elrob the story, he said we'd have to go and check what was on that film. A few minutes later we were knocking on our neighbor's door asking him to hand us the photos, to which he replied there were none. We had to make him crawl and get the camera with his teeth, open it up and give us the roll inside. The police came later, investigated the incident and issued us a warning not to bother him or go within a certain distance of his property.

* * *

I started thinking, since I had moved to a new continent, a new world, how to avoid confrontations, resolve conflict and defuse situations. My true motives for having left Lebanon, after all, were to evade the vicious cycle of violence and start a new life. If I had any deception, frustration and spare energy, I thought I would save it for the gym and channel it properly It was then that I began noticing common wisdoms and viewpoints among the great authors and masters of war-craft I was reading:

- Any fight, no matter the form or style, is a balance of stamina, distance and timing.

- War was nothing other than an individual fight on the collective scale.

- War can never reach a final verdict nor a perfect settlement.

- You can win a thousand battles but never conclude a war.

- In order to win, one must first know oneself and one's enemy.

- The greatest victory is that which required no battle.

- There are win/lose and lose/win circumstances which are delayed forms of lose/lose situations, but there is as well a unique win/win situation where no one has to lose.

- Weapons are un-grown boys' toys for defending their beliefs, egos and emotions in compensation for their incapacity to use their God-given spiritual gift.

- The human spirit is formed by the knowledge and ideas we instill in it.

* * *

When one is moving and traveling the world, all senses become sensitive to the stimulations around, and the acceptance or rejection of the stimuli will depend to a certain extent on the depth of the stereotypes, biases and convictions ingrained in the brain, but what was the end game for all this human-generated tragicomedy and self-produced theatres?

Having experienced actual fear alongside physical pain on gym floors and in fight rings, I believed in having a good chance of acquainting myself with these questions. After all, my mindscape and whole way of living were undergoing major overhauls, and I thought now (or never) was the time to start using the trust God had fitted on my shoulders.

When one is in dire need, the brain digs into abysmal resources. I needed clarification about the true motives behind every new word, expression, manner, or emotion I was stumbling upon. And it struck me back then, that behind every tangible one prowls a hidden microscopic one, undetectable to the naked eye in a never-ending loop of cause and effect, an endless chain of action/reaction. I was trapped, unable to connect frankly with my surroundings.

Confusion and frustration followed as I was forced to copy and mimic actual trends and patterns, trying to adapt them to my old self. I set my mind on tracking all the way down to the roots, finding and excavating the reasons behind every behavior I stumbled upon with others, for better or for worse. It was a big ambition.

2. An Unexpected Encounter of the Third Kind

One evening, after a long day at work, I was walking back home, sniffing the fragrant summer breeze trying to shed some calories and bring out more muscle definition. I was looking in the direction of the traffic before crossing the road when my gaze got hooked on a piece of paper pinned to a wooden pole, flapping in the wind. It bore a picture of a colored cross surrounded by a circle with a few feathers attached to it. As I approached under the streetlight, it read:

Native American Meeting and Smudging Ceremony
Next Tuesday, 10am.
15601 W. Sunset Blvd – Pacific Palisades
No dress code – Welcome to All

I had watched Native Americans on the screen, but never in my life had come face to face with one. In books and screenplays they were always depicted as valiant warriors with a great heart, a lot of wisdom, and living close to the earth they called Mother.

This was my lifetime opportunity. I was excited, and thought I would get the Native Americans' esteem with my pumped up muscles and aloof attitude. On that date I had to take a day off from work in order to attend the meeting.

* * *

The hall of the Center was spacious and high, and there was a sign indicating where the gathering was taking place.

As I stepped in, there was silence. People were already sitting in a circle; I could sense from their facial expressions that some were old-timers, others novices. A few minutes later a man and woman walked in from the door; he was tall and slender with tanned skin and the build of a hardworking chap, wearing a brimmed hat from under which long black hair fell down his back. His eyes were gleaming, impenetrable, but his face was placid. The female was very pretty, fit and tall, dressed in a traditional fringe dress with bead and feather detailing.

There were greetings from the audience then both sat down cross-legged at the top of the circle. Silence ensued again for a few seconds as everybody waited for a hint when the man would start talking. He spoke calmly, welcoming us and thanking the Great Spirit for the beautiful day. He then made a sign to his companion, who stood and opened a leather bag from which she took out a bowl, a feather and a collection of colored tissue packs.

She picked a pinch of herbs from each pack, placed them in the handmade bowl and ignited a match to light them. While she was doing this, the man introduced himself as Paco, which meant 'eagle' in his culture, and the woman's name as Meda, the 'prophetess'. The last time they visited this Center, he said, was two years ago when they came to talk about Sundance and Vision Quests. Today the subjects of their visit were the Medicine Wheel and the Four Directions.

Before he started discussing the topics of the evening, he proposed to open the event with a smudging ceremony. There were nods of approbation along with some yeses from the audience. I was totally ignorant and much intrigued by what this smudge ceremony could be, and consequently I felt tense and observed closely.

Paco stood by Meda's side and blew a few times into the bowl to enliven the fire, then took it from her hands and started reciting a prayer while directing the smoke into the four corners of the room with the feather. We could hear him intoning:

"May your hands be cleansed, that they create beautiful things. May your feet be cleansed, that they might take you where you most need to be. May your heart be cleansed, that you might hear its messages clearly. May your throat be cleansed, that you might speak rightly when words are needed. May your eyes be cleansed, that you might see the signs and wonders of the world. May this person and space be washed

clean by the smoke of these fragrant plants.
And may that same smoke carry our prayers,
spiraling, to the heavens." [3]

When he finished, he turned to his companion and offered her the smoke from which she began making movements similar to freshening up the face and body with her hands. After she'd finished, she took the bowl from him, and he proceeded in the same way. Once he was done, they both turned to the first person on their right. Paco stood there in front of him, eyes closed for a few seconds before reopening them and offering him the smoke. The visitor apparently knew what he was doing as he proceeded so self-assuredly. People would wait until the Native opened his eyes, do the ritual with their hands and the smoke, then give a nod as a sign of completion.

Paco and Meda kept going around until they reached my destination. The Native stood there in front of me, his eyes closed. I could hear his breath amid the silence, while time felt like eternity; it also felt as if all gazes were focused on us. When he opened his eyes, I imitated the ritual in accordance with what I had seen and nodded my head toward the end to signal completion.

Once the circle was complete, Paco and Meda returned to their initial places. She lowered herself to the floor, placing her palms over her knees and sitting cross-legged, while he remained standing and started talking.

"The medicine wheel is a circle with a cross in the middle. It represents the four directions: north; east; south; and west. Even though the four directions are opposite to each other, they are always connected by the cross in the middle as well as by the circle connecting the edges of the cross. There is also the space above and below the circle which makes six directions and therefore six dimensions. And finally the center of the circle and the cross which makes the circle seven-dimensioned.

"There are colors in the circle representing the different races of people in the world: yellow for Asia; white for Europe; black for Africa; and red for the Americas. In an ideal world all the colors would be able to overlap with each other and mix. Everything in this world is a gift offered to us by Mother Earth and the Great Spirit.

"Besides the colors, the four directions also represent the four elements: fire; air; earth; and water, and the four aspects of life: spiritual; mental; physical; and emotional. Our health is dependent on the balance of all these elements; therefore, illness is seen as an imbalance in this wheel. In ancient native medicine, the healers helped people find their balance between spiritual, mental, physical and emotional aspects, hence prompting the patient to take an active role in the healing process, while in modern medicine the patient assumes a

passive role and relies on the doctor to treat him. Whereas the traditional Native American medicine approach is holistic and treats the four aspects of the human being, modern doctors are often called physicians because they tackle only the physiological side of a human being." [4]

He continued,

"When we appreciate the beauty, virtues and generosity of this Earth, we live in harmony and peace, and our righteous wishes shall be answered."

Sundance, Vision Quests, Holy Mother Earth and the Great Spirit: too many new notions I was coming across for the first time. My mind was racing, trying to digest all this new information pending on my senses, while my brain struggled to find space to sort them out, make sense and put order to these new interpretations.

Paco closed the seminar with renowned Native American words of wisdom:

"Our grandfathers warned us a long time ago that only after the last tree has been cut down, only after the last river has been poisoned and the last fish caught, only then will we realize that money cannot be eaten." [5]

Everybody applauded, then stood up and approached Paco and Meda to converse with them. Meda went to the door and invited us into the hall for refreshments. I waited for the crowd around Paco to subside then got closer to initiate a conversation.

As I was approaching him, I could sense his intense gaze, full of intent yet still impenetrable.

I thanked him and told him I was honored to be attending my first Native ceremony. He smiled and replied:

"You are always welcome. If you hadn't come forward, I would have sought you anyway. When I stood, eyes closed, across from you, I could feel strong vibes yet uneven, in disarray. You are too tense and on your guard, as if something is about to happen. Chill out, learn to relax, ninety-nine percent of the time nothing happens. And when it does, who cares? Better deal with it in a cool manner than always be defensive."

On that day, I left the Center feeling totally exposed, disarmed. My thoughts were racing at the speed of light; I could feel something in my mind was shifting. It also felt like a strange energy was invading me, bursting in my whole body, pointing to another journey, another direction.

3. Old Friend and Foe

Ever since the Native American encounter, my mindscape had been undergoing tectonic changes. I had seen and experienced with my own eyes a different way of interpreting and explaining the world. It dawned on me that tackling the big questions and giving them such succinct and practical representations as Vision Quests, the Circle of Life and the Medicine Wheel made more sense and was far more honest than what I had been previously taught. It felt for the first time there were alternatives to the collection of beliefs I had so vehemently quarreled for and protected, and which caused me and my peers many differences and complications. I was also walking light, with the feeling of never being alone, always in good company, safe and close to the earth.

Paco had mentioned something about the stars, the trees and all nature being witnesses to our thoughts and deeds. I had neglected these true friends and other aspects of my life for too long, and now was the time to elicit their help. The public library was not far from where I lived, on the corner of 6th Street and Santa Monica Blvd, and for a while it became my sanctuary. Each day after work I would skip the evening gym session and hang out on different levels, sometimes on a couch, other times on the floor until the closing hour, searching and considering any thought or idea that would provide me with an answer, an explanation, and guide me through my obligation. I had embarked on a new quest that started with human sciences and popular culture.

* * *

The most obvious section to begin with was religion and philosophy; having bumped into it at school, it was the easiest for me to engage. I was about to reconcile myself with an old friend and foe: the book from which I had divorced myself a long time ago because of the substance and structure they presented it with. I'd felt the need to take some distance back then, to reflect on the natural order of things rather than getting a diploma for my wall and a title that would land me a boring job based on hierarchical status and remuneration, inevitably leading to the conventional rat race.

Religion and philosophy were extensive, and sprang off the face of this planet from different eras and geographical locations. Every culture fashioned scholars, who left their imprint in history's records showing the path they followed to deal with various issues and thorny human relations. They had a past evolving from Ancient to Medieval, Modern Eastern to Western, religious to secular. Rationalism, empiricism, religious existentialism or spiritual philosophies presented different approaches to handle the questions of life and death, and the proper way to pass one's time on this precious planet. While in the West, the earliest and most documented accounts were the Greeks, at the same time, elsewhere around the globe, there were Chinese, Indian, Japanese, Persian, Arab and North African philosophies.

* * *

In China, the Three Teachings referred to Taoism, Confucianism and Buddhism.

The origins of Taoism are attributed to Zhuang Zhou and Lao Tzu reputed author of the famous *Tao Te Ching* or *The Book of the Way*, around the 5th century BC.

The truths of Tao:

- Everything is a differentiation of one infinity
- Everything changes
- All antagonists are complementary
- There is nothing identical
- What has a front (visible side) has a back (invisible side)
- The bigger the front, the bigger the back
- What has a beginning has an end

The Tao does not speak nor blame, takes no sides and has no demands of others or expectations.

On the other hand Confucianism, often referred to as a religion, was an ethical and philosophical system founded by the Chinese philosopher Confucius. It appeared at the same time as Taoism and developed its metaphysical and cosmological parts later under the Han dynasty. Some scholars believed that Lao Tzu was the teacher of Confucius as he was an older man. Confucius is famous for his axiom, *"He has not lived in vain who dies the day he is told about the way."*

* * *

In India there were also three schools of thought. Hinduism was considered back then the orthodox form of tradition, but there were also Buddhism and Jainism as unorthodox philosophies.

Hinduism is a philosophical religious system coming from the book of creation called the *Vedas*. The book is thought to have come as revelations in an authorless text, to be the work of deities and is honored by the six mainstream systems of Samkhya, Yoga, Nyaya, Vaisheshika, Mimãmsã and Vedãnta.

Buddhism, a nontheistic religion founded between the 6th and 4th centuries BC by Gautama Buddha, translates into *'The awakened one'*. It relies on the empirical evidence of the senses and professes a belief of cause and effect called Karma, which equates to everything being the results of the past based on every thought and action in this life and previous life cycles.

It introduces concepts like *Dharma* or reality and establishes four noble truths:

- The first noble truth is the existence of suffering, from birth to death. Sad it is to be joined with that which we dislike. Sadder is the separation from that which we love, and painful is the craving for that which cannot be obtained.

- The second noble truth is the cause of suffering: lust. The surrounding world affects our senses and begets craving that claims immediate satisfaction. The illusion of self originates and manifests itself in a cleaving to things. The desire to live for the enjoyment of self entangles us in a net of sorrows. Pleasures are the bait and the result is pain.

- The third noble truth is the cessation of suffering. He who extinguishes self will be free from lust. He no longer craves and the flames of desire find no material to feed upon, thus they are extinguished.

- The fourth noble truth is the middle path that leads to the cessation of suffering. There is salvation for him whose self disappears before truth, whose will is bent by what ought to be done, whose sole desire is the performance of his duty. He who is wise will enter this path and make an end to suffering. [6]

Buddhism offered eight steps known as the Noble Eightfold Path to free and align ourselves with the middle way:

- Right Understanding
- Right Intention
- Right Speech
- Right Action
- Right Livelihood
- Right Effort
- Right Concentration
- Right Mindfulness

While Buddhism does not deal with, hence avoids, the questions of metaphysics, Jainism dwells right on it. It professes a doctrine of trans-theism which is neither theism nor atheism, but a form of belief in independent existence of soul and matter, and the absence of a Supreme Being or creator. Followers of Jainism believe in Karma as the governing law of life, in non-violence and the multiple relative facets of truth or morality. They also believe ethics are the key to the liberation of the soul.

* * *

African philosophy dates as far back as Ancient Egypt and spread to four major regions: North Africa; West Africa; Central Africa; and the Horn of Africa. One text of utter importance which influenced Western thought is *The Kybalion*, a book that claims to have been written by Hermes Trismegistus, who earned the name 'Thrice Great' for being knowledgeable in the three wisdoms of the whole universe: alchemy;

astrology; and theurgy. Hermeticism inspired many, among them Saint Augustine, Saint Thomas Aquinas, Isaac Newton, as well as Rosicrucianism and Freemasonry.

The seven principles of Hermeticism: [7]

- The principle of mentalism
- The principle of correspondence
- The principle of vibration
- The principle of polarity
- The principle of rhythm
- The principle of cause and effect
- The principle of gender

* * *

From a different epoch and geographical location, thoughts were developed under the Abrahamic philosophies, from which creation, life and death, and ethics embodied by the Ten Commandments gave birth to the *Bible* and the three monotheistic religions.

Later on, in Persia, a type of semi-dualistic monotheistic religion based on the existence of one supreme god, Ahura Mazda with feminine/masculine dualistic aspects, was introduced. It was known as Zoroastrianism after its originator Zarathustra, who is believed to have dwelled east of the Caspian Sea in the 6th century BC. It stipulated that good deeds through free will shall lead to happiness and keep the chaos at bay. It also believed in the end of days and judgment day, which shall revive the dead from their graves in addition to restoring the world to its original state.

* * *

After many nights spent at the library, fully immersing and engaging myself in the subjects, came the turn of the books I'd fallen in love with as an adolescent: Greek philosophy. In school, the clarity and interest of the topic one studies is stirred or diminished by the teacher's passion, subject knowledge and willingness to trigger the students' curiosity, hence the core of teacher/student relationship. Greek philosophers were organized under three timelines and categories: Pre-Socratics; Classical; and Hellenistic.

Socrates, Plato and Aristotle were considered classical and were already familiar to me; consequently those studies went rather fast and easily. However, on that day I made quite a discovery. A Pre-Socratic philosopher, who'd lived between the 6th and 5th century BC and was a disciple of Anaximander, had sought in his lifetime to reconcile reason and religious beliefs. He believed the cosmos was constructed in spheres and that ether was the arch of everything. He also had an opinion on infinity, life and death, the esthetic ideals of life, as well as other scientific discoveries. But most importantly, he was the precursor of animal rights advocates and believed in the transmigration of the soul, something he called *metempsychosis*.

His name was Pythagoras, and his work was seminal. It inspired Socrates and Plato. Pythagoras's idea that the cosmos was constructed in spheres was an interesting thought, and more so since Paco had also made allusion to it in the Circle of Life and the Medicine Wheel theory.

Socrates was next in the series. He was a most honorable man who died for his principles, made to drink poison after refusing to apologize for accusations laid against him of corrupting the youth, criticizing the social fabrics of Athens and people in high places. He questioned the collective notion of good and evil and of 'might makes right' at a time when Athenian democracy was in decline and Sparta was winning the war against it. He talked about ethics and the proper way to conduct oneself, and was described as the 'gadfly' of Athens; a gadfly, figuratively speaking, being an annoying person who criticizes others, pushing them into action.

According to Plato, Socrates's life as a 'gadfly' began when the Oracle of Delphi asserted that he was the wisest man in Athens, while Socrates thought otherwise and went to prove the Oracle wrong. He started roaming the streets of Athens, testing people's knowledge as well as the Oracle's prophecy, only to discover she was right. While he knew he was ignorant, most people thought they knew a lot. He drew the wrath of others for ridiculing them too much in public and was therefore judged, sentenced to death and put in prison awaiting his fate.

His friends bribed the prison guards to let him escape, but he refused to run away, justifying that if he did indeed run away, it would suggest he was afraid of death, which he was not, and his friends would be liable to face justice for helping him escape. He would have broken the social contract that bound him to the city, for which he assumed total responsibility.

Socrates is often referred to as the founder of Western philosophy, and had a probing question-and-answer style, precursor to pedagogy. Several renowned quotes are accredited to him: "*No one desires what is bad*", and "*If anyone did something bad, it would be out of ignorance or lack of free will*". He assumed virtue to be equal to knowledge.

His student Plato was more into politics. An important work of Plato's was *The Republic*, in which he suggests that there will be no justice in cities unless they are ruled by philosophers. But he later wrote two other books, *Laws* and *The Statesman*, in which he changed his views. In *The Statesman* he deems it preferable for a city to be ruled by a lawman, because a wise man will not be understood by all and therefore will be misjudged, while the lawman can judge everybody.

After acquainting myself with the classical works, I completed the journey with the Hellenistic. There were a few interesting characters, among them Diogenes of Sinope, the cynic, a very controversial man who adopted a frugal lifestyle close to poverty. He strolled in the streets of Athens during daytime with a lamp in his hand looking for an honest man, and believed virtue was better revealed through action than by words. His philosophical stunts included begging for a living and sleeping in a big jar on the marketplace. He also criticized the social values and institutions of his time and was a stark faultfinder of Plato whom he accused of misinterpreting Socrates; he even went as far as to sabotage Plato's lectures. Diogenes was the only one to mock Alexander the Great in public when the latter asked him to teach him wisdom. His philosophy was passed on to another great Hellenistic philosopher, Zeno of Citium, who developed it into the school of Stoicism.

Zeno the Stoic was born in the city of Citium, Cyprus in 334 BC and founded the Stoic school of philosophy, based on the moral ideals of Diogenes. He taught about goodness and peace coming from living virtuously in accordance with Nature's laws and that virtue could only be revealed in action, not in words. He loved to dwell on intellectual inquiries, had a dislike for extravagant and loquacious speeches and preferred the company of the few to the many. He divided Stoic philosophy into three parts: logic; physics; and ethics. The Stoic school taught that we are responsible for our thoughts and deeds, that a sage is a person of moral and intellectual principles, and distinguished between determinism, freedom and free will.

Next on the shelves was Epicurus. Born in 341 BC, he was the founder of the Epicurean school of thought which advocated a lucid state of tranquility called Ataraxia coming from rebuffing the hopes and faith of an afterlife, not fearing God and avoiding politics. Death was the end of the body and soul for him and should not be feared. God neither wants to reward nor punish us, and the universe's action and motion are due to the interactions of atoms moving in empty space.

He also recommended surrounding oneself with good, affectionate and trustworthy people.

Another version of Epicureanism was Hedonism, which derives from the Greek word for delight. It is said to have been founded by Aristippus of Cyrene, a student of Socrates, and stipulates that man's ultimate goal is to avoid pain and seek unconstrained pleasures without infringing on others' rights, which was a bit of a paradox since it is difficult to go after unrestricted pleasures without doing so.

Epicureanism was a more refined and ethical system because it advocated modest pleasures, mostly freedom from fears in life and death, and that knowledge and positive relationships lead to peace and tranquility.

Marcus Aurelius, a Roman emperor born in the 2nd century BC, is most renowned today for his book *Meditations*. He was considered one of the greatest Stoics of all time for having maintained calmness in the face of conflict and calamity, encouraging a philosophy of service and duty. He is quoted as saying:

"Do not then consider life a thing of any value. For look at the immensity of time behind you, and to the time which is before you, another boundless space. In this infinity then what is the difference between him who lives three days and him who lives three generations? Why do you hunger for length of days? The point of life is to follow reason and the divine spirit and to accept

*whatever nature sends you. To live in this way
is not to fear death, but to hold it in contempt.
Death is only a thing of terror for those unable
to live in the present. Pass on your way, then,
with a smiling face, under the smile of him who
bids you go."* [8]

All these men I encountered in philosophy were
great and deserved the designation 'prophet', but
did not exploit our fear of death and guilt of living.
There must have been something I hadn't discovered
yet; something philosophy did not elucidate. I had to
redirect my inquiry.

* * *

My body had rested for several months now,
following a three-day-a-week morning maintenance
routine at the gym while skipping the evening
sessions altogether. I noticed overall improvements in
my endurance and strength due to the unused energy,
and something called ATP (adenosine triphosphate)
stored in the muscles that I was now using for my
brain activity.

Over-training is one of the major problems
sports enthusiasts face. When we engage in sustained
physical effort, the body produces endorphins which
we all want to stimulate in our bloodstream, since they
reduce pain and make us feel self-confident and happy.
I missed training, but mostly my training buddies,
especially the guys I used to communicate with purely
via body language, by way of trading punches and

martial arts. It had been a long time since I'd last laced up my gloves and bitten into my mouthpiece.

* * *

It was traditional boxing that evening. The stairs leading to the martial arts studio on the second floor had big steps; old English fonts embedded between red Japanese calligraphy lay engraved on the black wooden door, translating the famous Dojo Kun, Bushido code of ethics:

> *Strive for good moral character*
> *Keep an honest and sincere way*
> *Cultivate perseverance through a will for striving*
> *Develop a respectful attitude*
> *Restrain physical aggression through spiritual attainment* [9]

After greetings, swapping a few jokes and updates on the latest gym activities, I withdrew to the changing room to tidy up my gear and get ready. The smell of camphor floating around hit my nostrils, raising my pulse, while the friendly welcome at the way in was immediately replaced by severe and serious glares at the lockers' exit. There was no more room for jesting.

Training requires a degree of commitment: a sort of total concentration often mistaken for mind exertion when it is actually mind emptiness dedicated to the present moment, otherwise the body and spirit each depart in a different direction and we become prone to injuries. It usually takes a few rounds to warm up; some skipping ropes and shadow boxing will usually do, but each person has his own ritual. After the sweat is broken, it is either the static heavy bag or a few rounds of sparring.

When one puts on the gloves before stepping into the ring, the pulse goes up one more notch and the adrenaline starts flooding, no matter the level of experience or years of training. Sparring is a fight simulation applied at 50% to 70% intensity. The aim of the exercise is to practice with live ammunition, under semi-real conditions, what we have learned and countlessly rehearsed in the gym under strict rules and supervision. However, what distinguishes the honorable warrior from the common one is his code of ethics.

Safety rules comprised no hitting below the belt, if one's back is turned, if a knee touches the floor or the opponent is totally dominated. I hadn't tested my stamina since my last competition and so my shoulders and arms felt a bit heavy and rusty.

Kevin was my favorite sparring buddy: he was fast as lightning, and canny. When the bell rang, we touched gloves and started measuring each other's breadth and speed through assessing eye contact and body language. I was able to sustain the pressure he liked to impose at the start, but soon after got into the groove and tempo.

There are three punches in boxing: straight; uppercut; and hook, executed with both arms which brings the total number of punches to six, but one can improvise an infinite number of combinations with them, like the binary code with which all computer language is written. Gloves flew left and right; we rolled and danced, bobbed and weaved, advanced and retreated. The battle is always to gain supremacy of the ring by conquering its center. We hunted each other on every rope, circling from corner to corner, barely having the time to catch our breath before the next bell rang, and after a few rounds we were both on the brink of exhaustion.

It is the epitome of camaraderie and brotherhood to be able to shake hands and tap each other on the back after a good and honest fight, then get out of the ring and bind it with a few beers. Satisfaction and serenity settle in after extreme effort exertion; we all have a capital of energy which, if unspent, could echo back on us negatively. Boxing is a big fraternity lesson, not a hostile interaction nor is any martial art. In fact, many things in life are deceptively violent while seeming elusively peaceful.

Combat sport is a skilled and disciplined body language; mainly because men's call is to use the strength God endowed them with, while women's strengths are love and life bearing. If this call is not channeled and used properly in a supervised and regulated manner, it could turn to vice and evil. Any confrontation with precise rules of engagements, if consensual from both sides, loses its vicious and violent attributes; it becomes rather an art and a 'sweet' science. There is a parallel in politics; any enforcement of the law in an organized civilized society must meet two specific rules of engagement:

the justified and proportional application of the deterrent force, otherwise it will degenerate easily into misuse, abuse, anarchy and tyranny. Therein lay the merits of democracy.

Timing and distance are also important in a fight, as in any interaction, and these imperatives must also be respected in society to safeguard the intimacy, vital space, sanctity and integrity of every human being. Non-verbal communication is a relatively new science and has many branches, one of several being proxemics. The word itself was coined in 1963 by Richard T. Hall, a cultural anthropologist who defined the distances in interpersonal relationships as:

- Intimate (if they fell within elbow's reach)

- Personal (within arm's reach)

- Social (outside arm's reach)

- Public (4 meters away and beyond)

There were other nonverbal communication categories related to touch (haptic), body movement (kinesics), oculesics (eye contact), paralanguage (vocalics), and time (chronemics). The way we use these nonverbal communications is directly related to the culture, education and nurturing prototype.

At the new rhythm I was going, my life had become well organized and efficient. Paco's awakening words echoed in my ears: "*When I stood, eyes closed, across from you, I could feel strong vibes yet uneven, in disarray...*"

Since then I had been restructuring my life; personal, work and education. From early morning to bedtime, time was becoming more valuable: training; work; then reading were the order of the day. Having interrupted my education after school, at first I had to make a huge effort to keep my mind on the task in hand, then things took a new turn and my intellectual stamina braced for it. All of a sudden I could read for hours on end without tiredness or distraction. It was similar to training: the more you do it, the more natural and invigorating it gets. Reading had its own endorphins.

* * *

Each philosophical revolution prompted an evolution of the human brain and introduced new ways of thinking and perceiving the world. There were major shifts and stages experienced in some cultures that did not occur in others.

Western culture had four:

– Ancient period, starting with the Greeks up until the arrival of Christianity.

– A Medieval period, extending from the 3rd to the 14th century and dominated by theological treatises of philosopher saints, such as St. Augustine, St. Thomas Aquinas and St. Anselm, in an effort to Christianize philosophy.

– Between the 15th and 16th centuries, a third and very rich period began with the discovery of the New World by Christopher Columbus; this event altered the view that the earth is flat and revived the notion held by the Greeks that it is indeed round and everything in the Cosmos is constructed in spheres. At the same time, the Church incurred a *first narcissistic wound* in its anthropocentric doctrine, delivered by Nicolaus Copernicus and Galileo Galilei with their new Heliocentric Theory. A few decades later, in the 17th century, a group of intellectuals emerged from different parts of Europe and challenged the clergy's authority. The ties were severed with religion and a Social Contract was drafted establishing a secular environment within the boundaries of a civil society: it was the birth of Modern Philosophy.

– The fourth period started in the 19th century with Charles Darwin inflicting a *second narcissistic wound* to monotheistic creationism, and the Church creed particularly, with his Evolution Theory. This period still extends to our present time with the development of science, neuroscience and psychology, restoring reason to the Western world and extracting it from religious inhibitions, superstitions, induced fears and mental lethargy.

Some argue that Modern Philosophy began with Columbus, Copernicus and Galilei in the 15th century Renaissance, which coincided with an inclination toward empiricism, natural observation and rationalism in philosophy introduced by Desiderius

Erasmus, Bernardino Telesio, Michel de Montaigne and Thomas More. Others consider it was triggered by the birth of the 17th century Enlightenment Movement across Europe, with the likes of Thomas Hobbes, Baruch Spinoza, John Locke, René Descartes, Denis Diderot, Francois-Marie Arouet (better known under the name Voltaire) and Jean-Jacques Rousseau, mostly renowned for his *Discourse on Inequality* and *The Social Contract*. The Enlightenment Philosophers also developed the Modern Encyclopedia from its 1st century AD version *Naturalis Historia*, and AD 630 *Etymologiae*, in an effort to snatch people out of ignorance and religious obscurantism. They had a firm belief, like ancient philosophers, that only through reason and knowledge can we create a better world.

Concurrently, this thought revolution was accompanied by a scientific one led by Sir Isaac Newton, a physicist, mathematician and natural philosopher. Newton's *Principia* framed the laws of motion and universal gravitation. All these new ideas nurtured a heave in knowledge and led to the emancipation from religious dogma. Contemporary philosophy became more specialized. Analytical philosophy, for which Bertrand Russell was a pioneer, was shaped by logical positivism supporting that philosophical problems should be solved by emphasizing attention to language and logic.

In an age of industrialization, technology, information and overpopulated world that has become socially, politically and economically over-connected yet purposeless, religious zealots are staging a comeback and propagating their beliefs in a new worldwide deception scheme, sowing and exploiting once more existential fears from life variability. We are in dire need, today more than ever, of reconsidering a new way of living according to a new United Code of Ethics: an authentic multicultural agreement for a Global Social Contract.

The developments and innovations in human sciences, neurology, quantum physics, as well as noetic theory have finally bridged the gaps reconciling science with spirituality. The principles of Hermeticism, Pythagoreanism, Buddhism and the laws of Physics make sense after thousands of years of negligence and denial of the realities around us. It has become a duty before a necessity to wake up to the responsibilities laid upon our shoulders to shape our own future based on the reality in this life and the premise of cause and effect; and not some stick and carrot technique based on the promises of an afterlife and an expedition with a father-figure causing dysfunctional imbalances between genders and discriminations among humans from divergences in creeds, so-called faiths, and other childish pseudo-merits of abstinence or indulgence in this or that form of ritual, prayer or chant to numb the senses and qualify as earnest.

The interminable mind wandering and metaphysical speculation of philosophy in Europe took a new turn, and was henceforth converted to more useful and applicable ideas, among them psychology, sociology, humanism, linguistics and anthropology. Great minds like Sigmund Freud, Carl Jung, Jacques Lacan, Melanie Klein, Émile Durkheim, Ferdinand de Saussure, Sir Edward Burnett Tylor, James George Frazer, Bronislaw Malinowski, Franz Boas, Margaret Mead, Ruth Benedict, Claude Lévi-Strauss, just to name a few, made great contributions to the refinement of Western culture and the exploration of the human psyche and spirit. We owe them much today.

* * *

While the history of human thoughts crisscrossed at times, it departed at others through various crossroads and intersections. The origins and reasons of their inception and development didn't make much sense to me. Why do we need so much identification to these beliefs and ideas on this planet, and where was their source, cradle and birthplace? I was amazed by how much the human quest was obsessed by all these meanings, and consumed by these explanations and interpretations.

The libraries were full of books made up of collections of ideas which became beliefs as soon as they touched upon the fear of death or guilt of living. Our minds were hosts and recipients to these thoughts and ideas, beside the daily bombardment from the media, people's conflicting moralistic point of views and our synthetic environment. If we all need to breathe, eat, drink and keep our bodies healthy and warm, what was the function of these ideas we risked our lives for and held onto so dearly? It is clear that we have persecuted each other and committed the most hideous crimes in their name and not, as is often referred, for the resources.

The tools of living have evolved but the causes of conflict and persecution remain the same. A few hundred years ago there were no oil and gas or developed economies, as we know today, to fight for. So what was the reason behind all this contention? Birds of a feather flock together; they might bicker but don't commit such gratuitous crimes. If beliefs and ideas were the culprits, where did their difference shroud? Was it existential and divine as some claim? And that their application shall open, as devout bearded men proclaim, the doors of hell or heaven. Or did they have another purpose and function?

I had made progress in my inquiry, but knew I was facing a Catch-22: a loop that never ends, a spiral that keeps expanding. Every discovery raised the stakes higher and every answer bred more questions.

A book on the shelves caught my attention; might be the pictur e on its cover, or the title: *The Power of Myth*.

* * *

Joseph John Campbell (1904–1987) was an American Irish Catholic born in White Plains, NY. His family moved later to New Rochelle, NY where he studied biology and mathematics, but he later discovered his calling in literature and human science.

Campbell traveled extensively and lived

across Europe, where he learned French, German and Sanskrit. He met Jiddu Krishnamurti, who inspired him in Far Eastern philosophies, but he was also influenced by German philosophers Arthur Schopenhauer, Friedrich Nietzsche, and the Hindu Upanishads, the common book of wisdom for Hinduism, Buddhism and Jainism. He became familiar with psychology and anthropology through the works of Freud, Jung, Maslow and Grof, and taught mythology, writing about it extensively.

His bibliography includes *The Hero with a Thousand Faces*, *The Masks of God*, *The Power of Myth* as well as many a series of books on comparative mythology. Campbell saw four functions to the myth:

- Metaphysical
- Cosmological
- Sociological
- Pedagogical

And believed humans evolved through four stages:

- Hunting and gathering societies
- Agrarian societies
- The first high civilizations
- Medieval mythology, romantic love and the birth of the modern spirit

To Campbell, mythology was, "*The song of the universe, the music of the spheres, music we dance to, even when we cannot name the tune*". He is often quoted as saying:

"Follow your bliss. If you follow your bliss, you put yourself on a kind of track that has been there all the while, waiting for you, and the life that you ought to be living is the one you are living. Wherever you are, if you are following your bliss, you are enjoying that refreshment, that life within you, all the time." [10]

* * *

A myth is a tale which describes an origin. It usually relates to the creation of the world. Stories that do not tell about creation are considered legends or folk tales. Myths have a social function: people tend to adopt and imitate the figures and heroes in their myths as role models for their lives. The myth bridges between the conscious and subconscious minds, has a founding function, and is a binding force for a culture and society through its common story. Comparative mythology analyses the myths of different cultures throughout history, trying to find common trends and features among them, and involves the fields of linguistics, psychology, anthropology.

Every culture had its share of myths about life and death, the beginning and end of the universe, and interpretation of seemingly paranormal activity. The Greeks had their first and most extensive accounts in Homer's *Iliad* and *Odyssey*, which depicted the Greeks' Trojan wars. Greek mythology, like its counterpart philosophy, had a huge impact on Western civilization in terms of arts, literature and cultural values. They had a god for every aspect of life, and their gods had a family and hierarchical statuses.

- Zeus was a king, a sort of god of gods and husband of Hera
- Hera: goddess of marriage, mothers, childbirth and queen of the gods
- Poseidon: god of the seas
- Demeter: goddess of agriculture
- Ares: god of war
- Athena: goddess of wisdom, war and useful arts
- Apollo: god of archery, music, poetry, prophecy, medicine, and later god of the sun
- Artemis: goddess of the moon, the hunt, and young maidens
- Aphrodite: goddess of love and beauty
- Hermes: god of the roadways, travelers, merchants and thieves
- Hades: god of the underworld
- Hypnos: god of sleep
- Nike: goddess of victory
- Janus: god of beginnings, choices and doorways
- Nemesis: goddess of revenge
- Iris: goddess of the rainbow, messenger of the gods

And there were many others.

After several months of unrelenting effort, I was able to peek at the world from our ancestors' perspective; my hunger and thirst for ageless Greek wisdom never faded. Their gods made more sense to me, had practical purposes, social functions and intervened in the daily lives of humans. I was roaming in uncharted territories, and the urge for more became irresistible.

Albert Einstein once observed, "*As our circle of knowledge expands, so does the circumference of darkness surrounding it.*" My attention span was expanding; I was able to sustain hours of intellectual effort without distraction, boredom or tiredness.

Learning goes through four phases: [11]

- Phase I: Unconscious Incompetence
  (We don't know that we don't know)

- Phase II: Conscious Incompetence
  (We know that we don't know)

- Phase III: Conscious Competence
  (We know that we know)

- Phase IV: Unconscious Competence
  (We don't know that we know)

According to the VARK system of education, these stages take place through four sensory channels: Visual; Auditory; Reading/Writing; and Kinesthetic, the last involving tactile learning. People with kinesthetic abilities are generally known to be slow but solid learners, and doers rather than just theorists.

Generally we use all modalities, but one or two are more central for each one of us. Attention is like a muscle: the more we use it, the more it strengthens and the less it withers and dies.

* * *

In 1990 the war theoretically ended in Lebanon, but it never did. Real problems were never tackled or solved. The two sides exchanged mutual niceties face to face, said that they were brothers without addressing the real issues and core differences. Each protagonist hid a knife behind his back, for when the quarreling kicks off in the future they resume slicing each other.

Religion was a big problem. The three monotheistic religions, it has been said, originated with the same man, the same patriarch if you like: Abraham or Ibrahim depending on your race or culture.

Four thousand years ago, Abraham was an old man with a long white beard, married to Sarah, who at first didn't bear him a child. Supposedly, with Sarah's consent, he proceeds to conceive one with her Egyptian maid Hagar, who later drew the anger of her mistress and was asked to leave the premises. The name of the boy was Ishmael, and is thought to be the ancestor of the Arab people.

At a subsequent date, and under God's auspices, like in all Biblical stories, Sarah was able to bear Abraham's child. He was named Isaac, the founder of the Jewish nation. To test Abraham's faith, God submitted him to a severe test: to sacrifice his only child. This is where the story gets thrilling.

According to the scriptures, Abraham loads everything onto a donkey: some wood for the fire, as was the tradition at that time; a knife and the child; and proceeds to a nearby hill. Following God's request, he aligns the wood on the altar, positions the child on top and raises the knife to finish the job. But God intervenes at the last minute, holds his hand and the boy is saved by the bell. A poor ram, stuck in the bushes, trades places with the terrified kid and the story gets for now a happy ending.

Problems arise when Sarah dies: Abraham buys a cave in which to bury her and declares Isaac his only legitimate heir. Ever since that day, both Jews and Muslims celebrate and claim that the victim of this attempted infanticide and the aberrant, disillusioned father who heard voices in his head were their own.

Stories of this kind abounded in history books and provided existential significance and guidance to nomadic tribes living in harsh environments. Those people solely survived on hunting and presenting sacrifices to the gods in the hope it would bring them good fortunes and benedictions.

The stories of Theseus, 12th century BC, son of Aegeus, and Oedipus, son of Laius in the 5th century BC, were such cases, but they did not take on such a dramatic detour and existential, divine dimensions. Maybe because people of these myths were less emotionally inclined or had a different family structure and upbringing. Cultural myths determine the values and paradigms of the smallest building block in society: the family, and therefore the length of time before the umbilical cord is cut; in other words, the level of emotional dependence or independence.

Having lived in the Middle East, I have noticed all my life this inflated sense of self-importance everybody cultivates and that arises from an unconscious belief that they all know a God whereas others don't. In fact, their God is simply this model or archetype they aspire to be and feel the urge to defend so vehemently. It requires a lot of spent energy to maintain, protect and demand others to acknowledge, and is confirmed by constant soliciting for attention; otherwise a heightened level of insecurities is awakened, followed by resentment, blame, intimidation and aggression.

This emotional state is also highly opinionated, superstitious, corrupted, anti-authority and turns out to be incapable of team work or democracy, as it is very subjective and consumed by rhetoric, idolization, existential pretentions and conspiracy theories. No wonder the Middle East is in such a dire mess, and reliving this interminable tragedy.

The Judeo-Christian version of the West was different than the Oriental one, as it had undergone different phases. Besides having in the first place a totally different mythology, for which the credits go to Socrates, Plato and company, a more rational, social and universal form of religion was able to renew and emerge across Europe due to consecutive discoveries and achievements: mainly in science, literature and philosophy. In North America as well, the new European settlers finely altered their beliefs and ways of living to a more balanced and nature connected religion similar to an animistic form of Christianity after the frictions with the Native

American civilization, from which they learned a few parallels of practical purpose: the Holy Spirit and Virgin Mary were represented by the Great Spirit and Mother Earth, the masculine and feminine aspects of divinity.

Any healthy and sane mind wonders where the place for a father like Abraham or Ibrahim would be in our present society. Yet unfortunately, thousands of years and millions of innocent victims' spilled blood have fastened this Middle Eastern myth because of all the fears, wars and killings associated with it. It has consolidated its power in people's minds, and it will be very difficult to escape, disable or delete this written and resident program. Besides, any patriarchal society falls under the sign of Mars and is destined to endure the outrages of war.

When psychology states, "*Slay the father*" it doesn't mean it literally. It implies slaying Abraham or Ibrahim from our memory by balancing the feminine and masculine aspects of our humanity to achieve love, peace, and harmony. This myth is the instigator of this millennial crime and this ongoing political crisis. But how can we succeed when the *Bible* and many wise men prescribe honoring and respecting one's father and mother?

It takes a lot of honesty and courage to cut our umbilical cord, claim our independence and rearrange our lives accordingly. We all love our parents, at least most of us do, but we have to understand that we are foremost the recipients of their genes, consequently their Karma and subconscious mind. Therefore, if we don't take things into our own hands and correct the course of our lives, then our offspring and descendants will stay caught in the infernal cycle of love, hate and vindication. People who believe in a bearded Old Man up there in the skies and hoping for an after-life are in for a big surprise as they haven't been told the whole story.

Secular ethics and religious moralists operate on different wavelengths and modes: the first, on the rational level and the impulse of life for motivation; the second, on emotions, hopes, and the impulse of death and afterlife for inspiration. Bluntly stated, it is a culture of life versus a culture of death. Religion does not produce good people; it just benefits the few at the expense of the many, keeping them sclerosed introverts living in hope and denial of their most intimate fears and needs, breeding frustration and perversion. By directing this hindrance inward it turns out to be a very dangerous implosive or explosive trigger of combined violence.

* * *

Having been born a Christian and having attended catechism classes as a child, it always felt to me and some of my free-thinking friends that there were very unreasonable stories in the *Bible*, even in the *New Testament*. But we were taught to take them at face value and never question them. I mean, Jesus was a very nice and honorable guy after all, but why did he need to walk on water or play with fish and bread to convince his people and make them follow him? Life is a miracle without these stunts anyway. From the chirp of a bird to the majestic beauty of a butterfly, from the whistle and rustle of the wind to the glorious spectacle of the rising and setting sun, life is a gift of senses for which we are the predestined beneficiaries and appreciators. All faiths based on other demonstrations and expectations offer the wrong incentives, denoting spiritual greed, immaturity and ingratitude.

Jesus's merits were stopping the cycle of violence and promoting peace and love through his forgiveness formula, Luke 6:31: "*Treat others the same way you want them to treat you. If someone strikes you on one cheek, turn to him the other also. And if someone takes your cloak, do not withhold your tunic as well.*" [12] But other exceptional men did so too, such as Buddha: "*Hurt not others in ways that you yourself would find hurtful*", Confucius: "*Do not do to others what you do not want them to do to you*", Pythagoras: "*As long as Man continues to be the ruthless destroyer of lower living beings, he will never know health or peace. For as long as men massacre animals, they will kill each other. Indeed, he who sows the seed of murder and pain cannot reap joy and love*", Socrates: "*Do not do to others what angers you if done to you by others. No one does evil consciously and intentionally*" and Hinduism: "*This is the sum of duty: do not do to others what would cause pain if done to you*". So where did the difference between Jesus and all these other great men reside? Was the 'prophet' designation another assertion and pretension made by emotionally inclined people in need of existential answers and supplementary attention?

Regardless of the miracles he performed or their incentives, religious Christians argue that Jesus's message was unlike any other because it had the added value of stating the maxim positively, proactively — prompting us to take action, to do something for others we wanted them to do for us. Other philosophies presented it in the passive or negative form of "*Do not*".

But what if this was, and still is, the state of our world: that most people have different moods, needs, mindsets and are a bit, shall we say, devious and sadomasochistic? So what happens in this case? Shall we let them treat us the way they would like others to treat them if they enjoyed pain and suffering?

I was thunderstruck by this dilemma and felt the urgency to solve it as soon as possible, as it concerned me and others on a daily basis. What made Jesus, or other so-called prophets, different from other wise men that walked the earth from different cultures or geographical locations? Why didn't they get that divine label or dimension? Could it be that people from the Middle East thought so highly of themselves as to designate everyone who walked or spoke from their land a 'prophet'? There are different myths about creation that made more sense than the Garden of Eden and the Apple Tree. And if Christians honestly followed Jesus's recommendation and applied it daily to their lives I could walk into a church today and slap the priest and a few of his followers a couple times. Would I walk out unharmed?

If Jesus came back today and walked among us, how would we recognize him or treat him? Does he need to dwell in the streets of the Vatican, New York, Athens, St Petersburg, or should he go back directly to Jerusalem? Does he need to walk on air and multiply burgers, fries and Coca-Cola this time? Will he move around on a donkey, or hop on a motorbike and travel on the subway? Does he need to go barefooted in a long white gown or wear a pair of casual denim jeans and worn out Converses? Will he use the homing pigeon or Twitter, Facebook and the latest tablet, iPhone or Android? What will his external looks be? Will he be allowed to return as a female this time or does it have to be a male again to convey the messages?

There are many wise people delivering valuable messages nowadays, so why don't we listen to and honor them? Is it a prerequisite to be persecuted on a cross to become legitimate and accepted?

If Jesus came back today, people would probably reject, torture and crucify him one more time, then wait another thousand years before interpreting his messages any way they liked, adopting his archetype and the cross upon which they slew him as symbols and representations, without caring much about the true nature, content and purpose of the messages.

Part II

4. Blue Skies

In 1997 I moved to Daytona Beach, FL. to concretize a long-time dream of becoming an airplane pilot. Written and flight tests, dispensed by FAA accredited examiners, as well as two hundred and fifty hours of accumulated flying time were required to get to the next level. Having earned my Private single-engine license the previous year, I found Florida was the best place to upgrade it to Commercial multi-engine Instrument Flying Rules. The weather was nice all year round and the rates were very reasonable compared to other areas or countries around the globe. I met a few nice people attending the same establishment, but was dubious of others. Aviation is a gracious profession and it felt to me, at that time, they lacked the necessary skills or manners to earn it.

Barnes & Noble was a mile and a half away from where I was staying, so it was very practical to carry out my studies while keeping my other mind inquiries going. The flying school in the airport vicinity also offered an education area with a computer-based software to practice for the exams which was a plus for the American pedagogical system, particularly the kinesthetic part of learning. Fittingly, in one of his books, the French author Antoine de Saint-Exupéry compared the airplane window to a microscope through which one can observe and comprehend the earth.

Public transport was not among Daytona Beach's strong points, but the weather was perfect, it had pristine beaches, and the laws were very lenient regarding motorcyclists riding without a helmet, which made it a favorite destination for riders from all over the States. Each year around March they would meet and celebrate the Daytona Bike Week, an event involving racing competitions, concerts, street parties and festivities, and I traded my Japanese sports bike for a Harley Night Train for the occasion. Deland Skydive Center was also a few miles away, not far from the newly opened Sky-Venture Wind Tunnel simulator.

5.   Gaia

Her name was Gaia; I'd seen her couple of times at the drop-zone in Deland. She was extremely good-looking in a non-sexy way, not ostentatiously. In Greek mythology, Gaia was the Goddess of the Earth, mother of all creation.

One time, we were on the same altitude climb to twelve thousand feet. She exited the plane with open arms in a headfirst dive attitude, her black ponytail trailing through the clouds from her red helmet. She also had a butterfly tattoo on her neck which symbolized eternal rebirth, independence, unconformity, and rhymed well with the name she had been given. I thought she was very cool. Every time I walked into Barnes & Noble, she would be there with a book in her lap, squatting on the couches.

I went straight to the cafeteria on that day to get a coffee I thought would give me the impetus and inspiration to approach her. I didn't know what she was reading or the area of her interest but was now well armed with a philosophical background. And so, I randomly drew a book from the shelves and with my coffee mug in hand headed down the stairs leading to the lounge on the ground floor, where she was seated. The book title was *When Nietzsche Wept*, a novel by Irvin Yalom, an Emeritus Psychiatry Professor from Stanford University.

It took me a while afterwards to discover there are no coincidences in this world, just little events we figure out at times when our senses are wide open.

* * *

There was a wooden table separating an empty chair from where she was settled. On it laid a keychain and a notepad with a disposable pen that obviously belonged to her. After I'd sat, I took a few seconds to move my mug in a very deliberate way, trying to place it on the table, requesting acquiescence from my neighbor.

"May I?"

She lifted her eyes from the book and tactfully smiled.

"Sure."

She continued to look at me as I set my coffee on the edge of the table and smiled back at her.

"I think we've crossed at the drop-zone," she said.

I've always been appreciative of straight-forwardness and natural attitudes, not the concealed, twisted, over-enticing seduction game many engage in to blur, deceive and entrap the opposite sex.

"I thought so too. Do you often come here when you're not diving?"

She reflected my playfulness, holding her smile then responding calmly, "Yes, but there are other things going on in my life besides this activity."

"I thought you were competitive back there. I mean, your performance last time was, to say the least, outstanding."

"Thank you. I have a couple hundred entries in my log. One has to perfect what one ought to be doing; it is the most fitting way to achieve actualization."

"My logbook is not as full as yours. I started jumping in Belgium in 1986 then stopped, and just earned an A license."

"Skydiving is a very special sport; it has taught me a lot. Above all to face my fears and scrutinize myself."

"Indeed, it is the adrenaline rush that kept me going." I responded.

"It is more of a mental exercise. One has to be calm and ready before stepping out there. From the ground to the sky is a journey of awareness and self-understanding. The minute the plane takes off until it levels are stages of introspection and meditation. And when the exit door opens and the oxygen-scarce cold air mixed with the smell of burnt engine fuel fills the cabin is a moment of epiphany for every skydiver.

"So, what brings you to Daytona Beach?"

"Well, I'm trying to get back on track after a decade of wandering. I am also pursuing a Commercial Pilot qualification at Phoenix East."

"So you actually don't just leave a perfectly serviceable airplane in mid-flight, you fly it as well?"

"I can fly it. Otherwise I am here at the bookstore to further my personal education."

"May I see what you're reading?"

As the book changed hands, she looked at the cover and smiled.

"This is one exceptional book you've picked. Most of the events related in the story are true. They recount the transition period from philosophy to psychology in 19th century Vienna, Austria through the personal relationships between the philosophers and psychoanalysts who laid the foundation of modern psychology."

"Actually I am still a novice on the subject; the book just bode well from the shelves. My main areas of interest have been so far, philosophy and mythology."

"Psychology is an extension of those two disciplines, if you want. It is the branch which excavates and analyses the roots rather than dwelling on the endless loops of cause and effect and the eternal search for meanings. It rendered these disciplines more pragmatic by organizing them in systems and methodologies while establishing checklists and road maps to the aimless insatiable wandering of the human soul. Human Science is all somehow related."

"Hmm, you mean psychology is an accessible discipline? I can still comprehend it?"

"Of course you can, you seem like a smart boy. If you haven't read your book yet, it is highly recommendable for a start, as well as other books by the same author. I can share a brief history of psychology with you, if you care."

"By all means, please do. That would be most interesting," I reacted, trying to satisfy my curiosity, as much as becoming more acquainted with her.

"Well, I'd actually be very happy to. You would be my guinea pig for the finals. I am preparing a thesis on the subject."

"I don't mind being sacrificed for that cause."

"As you wish then, where shall we start?" She paused for a second to place her book on the table, shifting her body in my direction. "The etymology of 'Psychology' derives from the Greek words of *psyche* 'breath, spirit, soul' and *logia* 'study of'. It was coined in mid-16th century by Philip Melanchthon, a German Protestant reformer. Its origins are deeply rooted in philosophy and date back to the mental investigations initiated by ancient Greeks, like Thales, Plato and Aristotle, as well as Persian, Egyptian, Chinese and Indian sages who delegated us many interesting texts, primarily from Taoism, Confucianism and Buddhism.

"In 600 BC, cities in Greece had temples for Asclepius, the Greek god of medicine, to treat psychosomatic illnesses. Asclepius had also daughters like Hygeia, goddess of health and purity; Aceso, goddess of healing; Laso, goddess of convalescence; and Panacea, the goddess of universal remedy.

"In the 3rd century BC, the most famous temple for this purpose was on the island of Kos, home of Hippocrates, the father of modern medicine. The original Hippocratic Oath went as follows: I swear by Apollo, the physician, and Asclepius, the surgeon, likewise Hygeia and Panacea, and call all the gods and goddesses to witness that I will observe and keep this underwritten oath to the utmost of my power and judgment...

"It wasn't until the 19th century that psychology began progressing toward an independent science. In 1879, Wilhelm Wundt founded the first experimental psychology lab in Leipzig, Germany to study and explore the nature of religious beliefs, identify abnormal behavior and locate damaged parts of the brain. A few years later, in 1887, a second lab was established in the city of Göttingen by Georg Elias Müller. Another important figure of early German psychology was Hermann Ebbinghaus, who pioneered and developed the learning and forgetting curves; the experimental study of memory. At the same time, across the Atlantic an American philosopher/psychologist physician by the name of William James became renowned for his pragmatic views and for being the first to introduce a psychology course in the United States. He was a prolific writer as well, famous for the publication, in 1890, of *The Principles of Psychology*.

"Meanwhile, on another continent, a Russian physiologist by the name of Ivan Petrovich Pavlov embarked on experiments associated with temperament, conditioning and involuntary reflexes, known as Pavlov Principles and widely used in education. Pavlov influenced writers like Aldous

Huxley in his dystopian novel *Brave New World*. Many researches followed later in Germany and the United States by eminent figures such as Granville Stanley Hall, John Dewey, Hugo Münsterberg, until the emergence of an Austrian neurologist from Vienna named Sigmund Freud, who revolutionized the discipline by introducing psychoanalysis or the exploration of the subconscious mind.

"The book you are holding in your hands recounts this period of psychology."

"Wow, you mean this book and our encounter today were no coincidence at all?"

"You can call it that way!" she winked. "Carl Jung, a Swiss psychiatrist and friend of Freud, called occurrences *synchronicity* or meaningful coincidences if they occurred with no causal relations."

"Thank you for the introduction..."

"Gaia."

"Honored to meet you. I thought I'd noticed your name on the airplane's manifest the other day. I am Mario."

"Nice to meet you, Mario. So where are you originally from, and where are you heading to nowadays?"

She was quickly adapting to my upbeat rhythm, which not many can handle, and was now reining in the conversation.

"I was born in Beirut, and moved here a few years ago. Having attended French school as a kid, I always wanted to complete my education in English and fancied the idea of getting to the States, which embodied to me the land of freedoms and opportunities."

"Nice! What does freedom mean to you?"

"Don't know. Freedom of movement: big spaces, long interminable highways, nature, wilderness, Indians and cowboys...if you know what I mean?" I answered, taken by surprise.

"I see you are an adventurous person. You need a lot of vital space to fulfill your aspirations."

"Is that wrong doctor?" I teased her while moistening my lips with coffee.

"Not at all, that is very healthy actually. But no external freedom is real without internal ones: freedom from fears and freedom of thoughts and expressing what one ought to learn to express in a distinguished democratic manner. Nowadays with the mingling of cultures and civilizations a big misunderstanding or clash, as it is called, has sprung up. People coming from different backgrounds, traditions, values and family models have different concepts of freedom. It is very subjective, and so are its applications, often open to interpretations.

"You can observe the outcome in your daily relations from the distances people use and respect when dealing with each other and where they lay the limits of privacy, intrusiveness or aggression. Likewise: the respect for time, frequency of glances, eye contact, articulation and phonology. Do you know that the words we pronounce only represent seven percent of the messages we try to convey? A study undertaken in 1967 by Albert Mehrabian, an eminent Emeritus Psychology Professor of UCLA demonstrated that fifty-five percent of the message is transmitted by body postures and thirty-eight percent by voice tone. The Social Contract in every society is the only guarantor of these sacred coordinates of time and space and the founding convention of civil society."

Holy moly! That was a lot of substance that girl was flinging on me all at once, although I was familiar with some of the concepts and ideas.

"Yeah, I've studied the non-verbal communication you just mentioned in martial arts and find it very fascinating. I agree one can observe how people behave and adopt different stances and attitudes in their daily activities, but I'd never thought of it as cultural."

"Every culture, Mario, has established a set of standards and paradigms, to create a reality in which people interact to exchange the daily necessities of life. Today's clash of civilizations is actually a clash of these realities."

"Tell me about it!" I rejoined. "Coming from the troubled region of the Middle East, I've had the privilege to experience a few."

"And what have you discovered?"

"Well, to say the least, there are some very clear laws and rational conventions here in the West, very practical indeed and related to our daily requirements. However, back home the whole region is open to explanations and divine interpretations. You have drawn the big lines for your lives and constantly work on refining them, while in the Middle East they haven't yet agreed on which religion or confession to abide by or follow in their earthly dwelling."

"Any other distinction?"

"As a matter of fact, there is more open-mindedness and freedoms here like the ones you were referring to, and that might also be related to these well-defined and rational civil laws. You can see people transcending their creeds and cultural differences and living side by side. Discrimination and prejudice have become exceptions penalized by the law, while in the Middle East they are a way of life based on distinctions in beliefs, ideologies, obedience, and associations. People there might think they don't suffer from them because they are the norm, and point a finger to exonerate themselves every time they hear a story of discrimination in the West."

She listened carefully, intently, to what I was saying then started speaking.

"According to Abraham Maslow's *A Theory of Human Motivation*, human needs must be met in the following order: Physiological, Safety, Love/belonging, Esteem, and Self-actualization. As Maslow's hierarchy is as true today as when it was introduced in 1943, the basic self-actualization needs for some consist of highly subjective unconscious existential desires for immortality and need for meanings, addressed by spiritual inquirers, philosophers and psychologists.

"Freud founded his psychoanalysis school on the unconscious aspect of the personality. In his 1920 and 1923 theories 'Beyond the Pleasure Principle' and 'The Ego and the Id', he introduced the impulse of life or *Libido* and impulse of death or *Mortido* as the main drivers of our lives, justified with the will to pleasure and avoidance of pain. Freud placed great importance on children's early development, which he called *psychosexual* and categorized in five stages: Oral (sucking, swallowing); Anal (withholding or expelling of feces); Phallic (masturbation); Latent (little or no sex drive); and Genital (sexual intercourse). Fixation at a determined stage can trigger narcissism as a defense mechanism and generate mental peculiarities like dependency, aggression, obsessiveness, vanity and inferiority, among others. While a certain degree of narcissism is normal for self-preservation, it becomes pathological when a person shows five or more of the following symptoms: has a grandiose sense of self-importance; is preoccupied with fantasies of unlimited success, power, beauty and ideal love; believes he or she is special or unique; requires excessive admiration; has a very strong sense of entitlement; is exploitative of others; lacks empathy; is often envious of others; is often arrogant and haughty. Such signs fall into the category of NPD, or Narcissistic Personality Disorder.

"Freud's school of *will to pleasure* was followed by Alfred Adler's school of *will to power,* based on Friedrich Nietzsche's philosophy of ambition and realization of the highest positions in life, and later by Austrian neurologist/psychiatrist Viktor Frankl's school of *logotherapy* or *will to meaning*, inspired by 19th century Danish philosopher Søren Kierkegaard."

"Did you mention *Libido* and *Mortido*?" I muttered, as I had come across these two words before.

"Freud's student Paul Federn, also a native Viennese psychologist, coined the word *Mortido* from classical Latin as the psychical energy associated with the death instinct of self-destruction, in contrast to *Libido* or the instinctual psychic energy for life, sexual pleasure and self-preservation. While every school of thought offered a different approach to self-realization, I believe they were all at some point compensation for failing a human's ultimate purpose of *will to happiness*. The state of bliss, you must have encountered, great minds like Lao Tzu, Confucius, Buddha, Socrates, Epicurus, Zeno of Citium and Jesus advocated. But people looking for the path of least effort misinterpreted this ancient wisdom, falling into the tricky traps of desire for immortality and urge for meanings.

"Although Freud's followers split later and offered variations on his school of thought, while feminists challenged his views on female sexuality, every situation depends on the contextual and cultural preoccupations and concerns of its time. It takes similar problems to reflect on the causes. Nobody understood religion like Freud, and today's world is mostly troubled by it."

"That was quite a feat Freud pulled off in his lifetime. It takes massive effort to come up with so many inquiries."

"Yes, Freud is considered one of the most influential persons of the 20th century. But did you know that myth is founder of civilization?"

"Tell me about it," I pressed.

"You told me that you're familiar with mythology."

"Yes, I've read it mainly through the works of Joseph Campbell."

"You must then know that a myth is a story that offers explanation of the unknown. It was usually handed down to us verbally through history and contains archetypes: typical themes, characters and behaviors of human nature we all copy as roles in our lives."

I smiled. "I do."

"And that the difference between a myth, legend and folktale is the content: a myth deals with the questions of creation, life and death, a legend relates to an historical event, either true or exaggerated, such as Robin Hood or King Arthur and the Sword in the Stone, while a folktale is a bedtime story like *Pinocchio*, *Cinderella* and *Little Red Riding Hood*."

"That, I'm also aware of," I replied, trying to figure out where she planned to take me.

"While all these stories hold enough meanings and symbolisms to shape our perception and fathom our reality, they will take hold of our lives and become the main driver as soon as they touch upon the question of life and death. Like a computer's operating system, this belief system, which I would call CBOS — the Core Beliefs Operating System, will become the central platform from which all subsequent education, academic, professional and otherwise, will remain peripheral to circulate our thoughts, energy and attention.

"In this psychosomatic world running on quantum physics, every idea, belief, prayer, wish or suggestion has the potential of becoming a self-fulfilling prophecy. The myth is founder because it holds the key to balance between the impulses of life and death through the archetypal roles adopted by a culture and society. And impulses are like a pair of wings, Mario: if one is stronger than the other, a bird cannot fly."

"Are you implying myths created this world, Gaia?"

"To a certain extent, the myth shapes the reality in which we evolve, but it all depends on our free will, if we have any left. Free will is awareness and consciousness to walk the delicate balance of life between antagonists. '*No man is free who cannot command himself,*' taught a wise Pythagoras."

"Impulses of life, death, myths and realities?" I mumbled.

"While an alignment of consecutive letters constitutes a word, a word becomes a paradigm, a symbol representing an idea by association. An organization of ideas forms a belief. Words, ideas and beliefs are tools we use daily to generate realities within our mind's belief system, to create environments for interactions with others and exchange the tokens of attention on the ophthalmic (sight), auditory (hearing), gustative (taste), olfactory (smell) and tactile (touch) senses, thus stimulating our parasympathetic and physiological systems. While the classification of the five senses is attributed to Aristotle, the clarification that our knowledge of reality depends on our sensory perceptions is credited to Buddhism, but was later introduced to the West by Immanuel Kant in his 1781 epistemological work *Critique of Pure Reason.*

"Just like music notes from which emanate an infinite number of tunes and binary code in the digital realm, the tiniest structure of reality is the alphabet from which the sound of a letter comes. People create all kinds of scenarios with these sounds and letters, from history to religious books, from education in schools and universities to scripts for movies and their lives, daily news and gossip. We are the carvers, actors and spectators of our own realities at the same time, and this does not contradict the presence of a creator and giver of life. On the contrary, it proves the utmost wisdom and generosity with which this world and life were conceived. In absolute, an object has no reason to exist without an observer; likewise, this world does not exist without us as recipients, observers and appreciators. Our minds are the projectors of our own realities, and this world is a theater set before our eyes through our senses and attention, a self-feeding loop of simulation and stimulation, of projection and perception for the exchange of two things only..."

She must have sensed my incredulity at her revelations as she followed up: "I will give you an example. Think of reality as a movie in a theater. While the virtual picture you see on the screen depicts a struggle between good and evil, it kindles in you the same emotions of amusement, sadness, fear or boldness, and causes the same body tensions as it would in real life. What is the difference for you between a movie and a real situation?"

"I don't know — real situations have consequences, a movie has none?"

"Yes, but real situations have real consequences only if you act on them, while if you also acted on the movie situations instead of sitting in your chair you would deal with consequences. In both cases a stimulus is pending on your senses and you choose whether to act on it or not."

She laughed. "Every morning, people propose different realities for you from scenarios they have devised and perfected to balance their needs. Some are compatible, others not; you choose whether to accept or reject them. Reality is like a TV set, you can switch the channels as much as you want. It constantly morphs with time and space and is actually different from one era to another, one area to another — from one city, one street, even one room to the next, from their design to the people occupying them.

"Every city is a different field of energy woven by its inhabitants, their myths, archetypes, values, and the balance or imbalance of the impulses of life and death. These manifest in the way the inhabitants deal with antagonists, most conspicuously gender rights and their use of body language and non-verbal communication, within the boundaries of time and space. A street map will quickly reveal to you people's functionality or complication by how they configured their streets and how energy flows in their city. In fact, this street map is a projection of the neuronal networks and synapses of the same brains who designed it. The same energy or cacophony that exists and flows in their minds will circulate or clog in their streets: it is life's order or anarchy. Some realities are fluid, others are rigid. Many people have few realities, few people have many. It takes guts and initiative to leave the past behind and explore new horizons."

"Regarding what you are saying, Gaia, I am beginning to doubt anything is real."

"Of course nothing is real, Mario, other than two cardinal things. Reality is an illusion, a projection of our minds: albeit a script on a screen, a simulation. People confuse reality with life and life with reality, while philosophers are at pains to define it. Because reality is undefinable, ungraspable, it flows like a river. It is the water that carries the boat. It is just a medium for something else."

"I think I've heard about this river reality before. Was it Heraclitus?"

"Yes: 'No man ever steps into the same river twice'. There are numerous other metaphors; the words Maya in Hinduism and Dharma in Buddhism both designate the illusory nature of reality. One of the best descriptions is Plato's 'Allegory of the Cave'."

"Wasn't it about humans being chained to a wall in the darkness of a cave, from which they could only see the shadows of real things projected to them from a burning fire outside?"

"I see you've done your homework in philosophy. Yes, Plato also mentioned that only a handful of enlightened philosophers would be able to escape this condition and return to tell the people of the cave about the true world outside.

"Reality and life's games are infinite and undefinable, Mario. However, our roles fall into few categories."

"Tell me about it," I urged, growing impatient as this discussion seemed to be veering toward a fully-fledged psychology course.

"What Freud defined as *id*, his friend Jung dubbed *persona*: social masks we adopt among the many available in our societies as defense mechanisms to protect ourselves when we are hurt, worried, insecure and need compensation. Jung defined two functions for these masks: to make a certain impression on others and conceal our true nature. While the development of a mask is a normal preparation for adult life, it should be flexible and dispensable at a later stage. It should not become part of a person's true identity as it will inhibit psychological development and result in superficial conformism attitudes. The person will confuse their social mask with their true self and life's essence.

"Examples of masks are the costumes, statuses, titles and attitudes people assume at work and hang on to afterwards in their social interactions. A normal and healthy progression of this persona is called *individuation*: identification to the persona in early life; followed by *disintegration* when the excessive commitment to the social mask diminishes and dissipates; then *restoration* of a new more viable persona which does not hide the true self. Failing this progression will result in negative restoration of the old persona with feelings of bitterness, disorientation and inner chaos, then compensation with pleasures, power games and meanings.

"The same concept was later developed by pediatrician psychoanalyst Donald W. Winnicott who saw that early life nurturing was decisive in determining what he called this *true self* or *fake self*. Many factors, starting with the techniques the mother used while holding, bathing and feeding her child, and if the presumed attention was moderate and authentic, deficient or excessive, the baby will later extrapolate and transfer to the world by being independent and unaffected, or dependent and conformist. How the mother's early fostering impressed the toddler's senses will be a determining factor later in life, for the span and intensity, of its need for attention.

"The games people play in life to solicit attention are infinite, but the roles fall, according to psychiatrist Eric Berne, into three major categories: the Parent; the Child; and the Adult. These reflect the state of the people's ego, determining whether they're a parent-like control freaks, obedient, subdued and childlike, or mature independent individuals: a goal to achieve in Transactional Analysis therapy.

"A similar study was undertaken by Stephen Karpman M.D., a student of Berne. Known as the Drama Triangle, this study points out the similar roles people assume to get approval and recognition by attention. The defining characters of this triangle are the Persecutor, the Victim and the Rescuer. Each one is codependent, exchangeable and egotistically motivated by the other. One person may adopt a victim's role to make his opponent look like a persecutor and therefore get the onlookers' sympathy.

"One particularly interesting subcase of the Drama Triangle was coined the Stockholm syndrome by criminologists/psychiatrists Nils Bejerot and Frank Ochberg, in reference to the city where it occurred. The incident demonstrated the codependency and interchangeability of roles people consent to in certain situations.

"In August 1973, during a bank robbery in Stockholm, Sweden, several bank employees were held hostage in a vault. While the police negotiated their release, some of them grew sympathetic toward, and even went as far as defending, their abductor. Following their liberation after a six-day ordeal, some of them, mostly women, went on to visit their ex-captor in jail. The study uncovered an inappropriate sympathy had developed between the enduring victim and persecutor: a feeling of gratitude and misinterpretation of the act of keeping them alive as an act of kindness.

"The most fascinating thing, Mario, is that all these roles and games of parent/child/adult and victim/persecutor/rescuer are not only played on the individual level but also on the collective one, and in politics."

"Is the veil some women wear such an example?" I asked, as this opinion had been expressed on a radio talk show recently.

"There is such an element in the veil. However,

there is much more to it. We could get back to that later."

"But if reality is ever-changing and never the same, and people play infinite games within finite roles, hiding behind social masks to conceal their true nature and *true self*, then what is the endgame of all this tragicomedy?"

She paused for a second before pronouncing it.

"Love."

"Ha-ha-ha-ha-ha," I exploded. "Are you serious or pulling my leg?"

"I am not pulling anything yet, not even my rabbit." She pointed her index finger at me. "The three Viennese schools of *will to pleasure*, *power* and *meaning* were all compensations for the elusive will to happiness, we acknowledged. The games, roles and social masks people wear and play all share the same fate when one is not independent and honest. Since the dawn of time, from handcraft, agriculture and tending the land, to industrialization, transportation and telecommunication, our ways of living have evolved yet people still persecute each other, perfecting the art of war like no other species. People of the same values share and trade; they do not kill each other. The prime motives for war are not, as some claim, geopolitical interests and the resources, but beliefs, leading to compatible or incompatible belief systems and cultural values. Women's status and the elusive *will to happiness* dependent on self-actualization through freedom of will or repression, occupy the center-stage in this compatibility or incompatibility principle.

"Don't be impressed by uniforms, garments, beards, hats, ties and pitched speeches. Most grownups are white-haired children raising children while looking for parental authority replacement and directions. They transfer this parental authority to religious and political figures, and get touchy and defensive when challenged because they don't truly understand why they are defending this parental archetype. You can tell to which culture they belong by the balance of impulses of life and death visible on their social masks, and the level of their need for attention. This intensity shifts from one culture to another depending on the mother's early nurturing and the inculcated need for acknowledgment. Every interaction we initiate with others triggers a series of chemical reactions on the parasympathetic system from both sides, manifesting in physiological symptoms and alterations in the anabolic or catabolic rates — constructive or destructive body reactions. This is the essence of psychosomatics.

"Everything in this world is a medium for the conduct, by simulation and stimulation, of two things to which there is no third: love or hate in our hearts. We are ideas/beliefs carriers — reality generators: love or hate exchangers. This whole world is a spinning theater, a merry-go-round we create to exchange them.

"Voltaire declared a long time ago, '*God is a comedian playing to an audience that is too afraid to laugh*'."

I was speechless and gathered my courage with two hands.

"What is love, Gaia?"

"Let me ask you that question. What is love for you?"

"I don't know. Is it the common good feeling shared between two individuals on Valentine's Day?"

"Are you a romantic?"

"Not at all." I laughed. "That was just an attempt at humor."

"Most of the time, the feeling you are referring to is based on idealization and devaluation: the image we project onto others according to our own needs and desires. It goes like this: 'I love you, so you love me in return and I'll stop loving you, or hate you, as soon as you stop loving me'. This is not love but lust, followed by jealousy, accountability and negative emotions. Love is not also the collective commitment that excludes others in families, institutions or nations. It is the middle path hidden below the leaves of fears, worries and distractions. It is appreciation of the never-ending, ever-renewing, priceless present moment, while accepting life and death and day and night natural alternating phases. It is freeing oneself from past memories and future expectations and living in peace, harmony, awe and respect for the smallest particle of creation."

There was a long silence after she'd finished, until I dared interrupt.

"Where is this way hidden?"

"It is the rabbit hole in *Alice in Wonderland*, Plato's *Cave* and Socrates's *imperative* for self-discovery, if you know what I mean. The only way to transcend narrow mindedness, self-consciousness and subjectivity is through unraveling content from symbolism, and life from reality. The rabbit hole is your subconscious mind, Mario. How deep can you go into its introspection for self-liberation and karmic bill settlement? Your Karma, and that of the entire human race, is hidden in the subconscious and carved in the DNA. Karma, the subconscious and the DNA are the same entity under different designations. From self-knowledge come wisdom, virtue and love, and from ignorance: narcissism, vice and hatred."

All the ghosts and devils of my past were set free, flying before my eyes, awakened by her resonating words.

"If you don't dive into this well and undo your bad Karma, it will be passed on in your genes from generation to generation."

"But why is it so hard to do?"

"Because of the veil of illusion. People get entangled in the realities, their fake self and personas with which they decorate their existence, confusing them with their true self and true life, while centuries' old myths fasten their hold on their perception. Since the beginning of time, anyone daring to challenge public consensus was persecuted, imprisoned or executed. People live in fear, the most dreadful one coming from bloody religious wars. But do we want a god of fear or a god of love? Here lies the gatekeeper of our subconscious mind.

"Why do you think they say '*In the Name of the Father and the Son*' and '*Our Father who is in*

Heaven' and not *'In the Name of the Mother and the Daughter'* and *'Our Mother who is in Heaven'*? Man carries war and death, woman bears love and life."

"Yes, but they pray also for *'Mary full of Grace'* in Christianity," I jested.

"Jesus was the only one to give women their due rights in the three monotheistic religions, although these rights were later taken away by bigots. He was not the misogynistic type who needs to reduce the woman in order to communicate with her heart. God is not a man. She might be a woman, or neither, but definitely not a man. Whoever does not consider the woman his equal is a psychological dwarf.

"While all political systems pretend toward some kind of social justice in the wealth, health, education and legal departments, they all have two main benchmarks distinguishing them: women's status and the degrees of applied and accepted freedoms. The traps these political systems fall into are the same ones individuals suffer from, namely the *will to pleasure* in Capitalism, the *will to power* in Communism and dictatorships, and the *will to meaning* in theocracies. After all, we are the product of our Karma but also of our environment, producing possibilities or hindrances for self-realization and independence or remaining an adult child. Capitalism came from excess of democracy; Communism emerged from abuse and misinterpretation of socialism and theocracy from existential sickness, alienation, spiritual sadomasochism and self-flagellation."

"That's pathetic," I retorted.

"Every culture has determined its ways of living according to its explanation of the two vital questions of life and death and their respective influences, from which two vantage points emerged: existentialism versus pragmatism.

"From the first arose religious existentialism as a belief system, inspired by a tale of a snake, an apple and a Tree of Knowledge in a Garden of Eden, analogous to Pandora's myth. Pandora was the first woman created by the Greek gods, around 700 BC, in Hesiod's poem '*Works and Days*'. The unconscious motives behind these tales suggest the rightness and finiteness of living that monotheistic religions have so well exploited by laying the blame on the woman, producing a man's God, man's rules and a patriarchal society, hence creating gender imbalances. They backed all their morals with the premises of punishment, fear and guilt, generating inhibition, repression, frustration, and their natural byproducts: inward or outward violence. Centered on the impulse of death and rejection of life in hope of an afterlife, they produced a culture of death from a Religious Contract.

"On a different level, pragmatism based itself, in the 17th and 18th centuries, on the Greek philosophies of Stoicism and Epicureanism, developed into secular civil order which helped the West emancipate from the chains of religion. It was founded on equal women's rights, freedoms of thought and expression, respect for public and private places, and responsible tax obligations and contributions. Driven by matriarchal balance and the impulse of life, it emerged into an ethical democratic order, producing a culture of life from a Social Contract."

"What is the difference then between religious morals and secular ethics?"

"Subtle question, not many may be able to distinguish In a nutshell, morality is to ask others to treat you how you would like to be treated, with acceptance or rejection, reward or punishment as incentives. Ethics is to treat others how they would like to be treated and respect their choices and integrity, unconditionally, without any hopes or expectations of rewards or losses, something religion has missed all along. All religious dogmas are centered on converting others by force or proselytization.

"It makes a whole lot of difference. In the first premise the other becomes a means to you and in the second proposition: an end."

"Yeah, I've reflected on this one: Jesus's Golden Rule of '*Treating others the way you would like to be treated*' or '*The way they would like to be treated*', and scratched my head hard to solve it."

"The glitch in Jesus's Golden Rule was that it missed being consensually reciprocal, and therefore was open to subjective interpretation. How can you do something to others you wish for yourself? This is imposing your own will, needs and whims on others. Any rule to be universal should be subject to two criteria: be reciprocal and consensual. It becomes as you just put it nicely '*To treat others the way they would like to be treated*.' The difference between morals and ethics lies along these lines; morals use words and tell others what to do in a pedantic way, ethics do not use words but translate into acts and are based on consideration for the needs of others, without any prior condition or expectation of gains or losses. The merits of philosophers and psychologists, Mario, reside in providing us with clear checklists and honest roadmaps to explore the deep confines of the subconscious mind: the ultimate responsibility of every human being to 'know oneself' to be able to transcend narcissism and subjectivity. Religion instead transfers this self-knowledge to an archetype it calls God, everybody ambitions to imitate. Along with a theory of anthropocentrism, literally taken and genetically egotistic 'be fruitful and multiply', it turned out to be the quintessence of narcissism. Demography is the scourge of the 21st century. How can someone preoccupied so much by the saving of his soul and the multiplication and proliferation of his genes be compassionate, empathetic and understanding to others' needs and feelings? There is an intrinsic value in human nature beyond the social fabrics and masks; it is a fine dose of virtue versus vice, of love versus hate, accessible only though self-knowledge and emancipation from subjectivity and ignorance."

"But if love is self-knowledge and hate is ignorance," I reiterated, "how can we remedy it?"

"They put people on blind faith and hopes but hope is dope and faith is expectation and alienation from reality. God is not Jewish, Christian or Muslim and does not speak Hebrew, English, German, French,

Russian, Chinese or Arabic. God is the universal energy that flows through life and manifests itself in body language and non-verbal communication. Beyond ideas, words and shapes, all interactions are in fact attention management and exchange on the senses within the confines of time and space. Some people are driven by pleasures, others by power and meanings, but the three drivers are scenarios that generate power struggle interactions, for attention and acknowledgement, in win/lose or lose/win instead of win/win situations, compensating for the elusive *will to happiness*. We must excavate our past to undo our bad Karma, not dwell on it. Whoever is living in the past lives in expectation. This deficiency was set in motion by the dysfunction of the initial myth and family model that created imbalances in genders, inspired by the role of a father who subjugated the role of the mother, and consequently affected our own feminine/masculine equilibrium."

"And how is it possible to transcend this subjective and narcissistic condition after all these years?"

"Only by reconnecting people with reality; educating them in proper body language, and the respect for time and distances. Any society is edified and governed by conventions; there are three areas that reveal mostly the degrees of narcissism or humanism, and expose the levels of cultural roughness or refinement in an individual and community: how people deal with gender relations and sexuality, how they sit and behave at the table, and how they share the road and respect traffic laws, the tax code and public places.

"People are dying defending their ideas, whereas ideas are just tools to be used at face value on the exchange of attention in the love/hate equation. They get stuck in identifying themselves with roles, beliefs and metaphors, trying to swap them for an afterlife, indulging in religious and political ideologies instead of achieving the end product of balancing their opposite impulses of life and death, thus feminine/masculine sides to deliver their humanity. Woman plus man equals human."

"That is a genuine and legitimate equation," I reacted. "But beside all the philosophers, psychologists and feminists, I still see Jesus closest to our description."

"Jesus was a decent and honest man who spoke about love without any divine pretenses. He did not devise anything new, but came to remind us of ancient rules and wisdom discovered by very wise men ages before him. Still, people needed mystical meanings and attributes to alleviate their misunderstanding and denial of death, and so in time adapted his stories to the path of least effort with the most promises, instead of the arduous road for self-discovery.

"The legends of the virgin birth in a cave on the 25th of December, followed by the star's announcement, the three wise men, the twelve disciples, baptism in the river and the miracles of death and resurrection were all features of previous myths. The Hindu god Krishna in 3200 BC, the Egyptian gods Horus and Osiris in 3100 and 2500 BC respectively, and in 2000 BC the Zoroastrian god Mithra all shared these same elements. It was the Roman Emperor Constantine The Great, aka Saint Constantine, who in AD 313 co-authored the '*Edict of Milan*' with Licinius, forbidding the persecution of Christians and granting all citizens permission to worship whatever deity they pleased, merging all prayers, rituals and ecclesiastical grading under the Christian minster.

"There was no hierarchy in Jesus's time — no priests, archbishops, cardinals or popes as we know them. In fact, Jesus sacked these long-hat wearers, golden cross bearers, incense burners and icon idolaters from the temples. But they returned to settle the score, embezzling his messages. There were the rituals of breaking bread, sharing a good glass of wine, and the Golden Rule of Antiquity. But there were also cardinal vices and virtues, copyrighted by these religious zealots to justify their existence at the expense of people's fears and further the conspiracy. From the womb to the tomb; the moment a child is born, baptized, receives first communion, ties and unties the knot, to the day that person finally returns to dust and ashes, they started making money. That's besides the act of tithing or other ecclesiastic bureaucracies. Religious institutions have become God Corporations. The level of corruption and deceit in a cleric is most visible by the length of his beard and the size of his belly."

"That's very funny, Gaia!" I giggled. "Could you please expand on the cardinal vices and virtues?"

"Sure. The first virtues were defined by Plato and Aristotle. There were four: Temperance; Wisdom;

Justice; and Courage. These qualities were later reiterated by Jesus, but after AD 300 three more had been added as theological virtues: Faith; Hope; and Charity. While charity is most honorable, it is not exclusively a religious duty. Hope and faith, on the other hand, are tricky religious ploys and the reason people fall into the traps of denial and alienation.

"Faith has many faces and runs into fantasy, phantasm, hallucination and mental delusion. Motivation in life should be based on the impulse of love of life while accepting the inevitable natural process of death, not dreading it. Life is not a sadistic punishment but a precious gift we ought to learn appreciate properly, ethically not morally, with our free will, for the attainment of the ultimate will to happiness and achievement of our humanity, not let ourselves be driven by reward and punishment like subservient children. The god of religions is a god of fear who rejects this gift of the senses in the hope of bartering it for an afterlife. The real God is a generous God of universal love without mortgage, debt or compound interest, for which life can only be abundance.

"Do we want a God of love or a god of fear? We choose. If you kill in the name of god, your god is either a criminal or a weak incapable god who needs you to defend him. Either way, religion is a drug and a very dangerous one. Fear only begets denial, inhibition, frustration and aggression.

"On the other side there were seven cardinal sins: Lust; Gluttony; Greed; Wrath; Envy; Sloth; and Pride."

"I never thought of all this before. Unfortunately, as you assumed, everybody is expecting others to abide by these principles for their own sake in a moralistic way, rather than ethically and in consideration of others."

"Yes, this all goes back to where our discussion started. Existentialism is motivated by the metaphysical question of death and afterlife. However, some religions prescribe that the road to the afterlife passes through death or martyrdom. The inevitable results are an impulse and culture of death. Pragmatism on the other hand is driven by the question of how to organize and better our lives on this very precious planet; the end results are an impulse and culture of life. Two opposite, incompatible and antagonistic ways of living. Religious fanatics do not care about the beauty and pleasures of this life, and forbid anyone else from enjoying them. They want to blow everything up to get to the afterlife as soon as possible.

"Religion is a collective existential sickness stemming from the misinterpretation and misunderstanding of death, denial and alienation in life, and parental authority replacement. At the end of the day, it is a culture of life versus a culture of death."

"So you think religions are teaching hatred and not love."

"Some of them are, others are preaching love for the wrong reasons or incentives. Heaven and Hell are right here on Earth and the products of our state of mind, thoughts and imagination. If they were so sure of their faiths and their afterlife, they would leave us in peace and enjoy the company of their man god in heaven. But they are so unsure and insecure in their beliefs that they become aggressive and force everyone to surrender to their creed as they don't want anyone to appreciate this miracle while they miss it all. How could someone so preoccupied by his death and the preservation of his genes and identity transcend his own narcissism? This is the quintessence of greed, ingratitude and gluttony.

"There are two things that we can exchange, to which there is no third, regardless of spiritual, intellectual, religious or material discoveries and inventions; love or hate. All other claims are politics, power struggles and mass manipulation. God has given us a brain religious fanatics want to shut down. Throughout history, rational and brilliant people were all pantheists."

"Wow, slow down Gaia. Take it easy on me," I snapped back. "Now what is a pantheist?"

She untied her braided hair and chuckled.

"A pantheist is someone who does not believe in a personal anthropomorphic god, and therefore does not believe in anthropocentricism and creationism, but that god can only be revealed through the world around us. The word Pantheism derives from the Greek words *pan* meaning 'everything' and *theos*, 'god'. The foundation of Pantheism is as old as the Vedas, Buddhism and Confucianism. The history of philosophy also reveals for us many pantheistically inclined pre-Socratic thinkers like Thales, Anaximander, Anaximenes, Heraclitus, Parmenides and the Stoics. In the 17th century, Dutch philosopher Baruch Spinoza presented the concept in his book *Ethics* in response to René Descartes's dualist theory. Like Deism, Pantheism rejects revelations from books and religious authorities and affirms that God can only be discovered through reason and observation, therefore science does not contradict the creator but proves the utmost genius and wisdom with which the universe was conceived.

"All great men were deists and pantheists: Ludwig van Beethoven; Ralph Waldo Emerson; Henry David Thoreau; Charles Darwin; Carl Jung; and Albert Einstein to name a few. It takes honest soul searching. Religion has long pinned pantheistic ideas as heresy."

"But why do so if pantheists also believe in God?" I snapped.

"Religious people accuse everyone of infidelity, atheism or heresy as soon as an idea or belief diverges from their own. It shows how frail and how defensive they are. Karl Marx compared religion to an opiate for the masses, while Freud considered the god of religions to be an illusion and a collective neurosis based on the infantile need for a father figure which helped restrain people in early civilization. Today, with the development of civil society there is no need for it. Like a child, civilization has undergone stages of maturity and development. Albert Einstein wrote: *'A man's ethical behavior should be based effectually on sympathy, education, and social ties; no religious basis is necessary. Man would indeed be in a poor way if he had to be restrained by fear of punishment and hope of reward after death. I believe in Spinoza's God, who reveals himself in the harmony of all that exists, not in a God who concerns himself with the fate and the doings of mankind'.*" [13]

"I could not agree with you more. I've seen a lot of mayhem in the name of this God of the Middle East, where people discriminate, persecute and exterminate each other, then brag and pretend their religion and faith bring them mercy and salvation."

"Secular and religious minds operate in two different modes, on different wavelengths. Democracy's founding principles were equal rights for women and freedoms of thought and expression; it was founded on matriarchal equality, to women's advantage. Religious societies are patriarchal and run on the cult of identities and the rule of men. It is a Social versus a Religious Contract. This is where cultures are most incompatible. Democracy is not about expressing yourself as much as accepting others' criticism and refraining from violence, otherwise it becomes a one way democracy and milking the cow.

"If someone wants to immigrate to a different country, it means he or she was not initially happy or satisfied in the original one. All this migration without integration is collective suicide. Coming to a host country just to learn the language without embracing the values is even worse than non-integration."

"You promised to clarify the meaning of the veil, Gaia. Is this where the difference shrouds?"

"We live in a world of symbols and representations. The way we dress, walk and talk, how we decorate our homes, cities and environment yields a treasure trove of information about us. The simpler and clearer we are, the closer to god and nature. People using complex art and language are in for the forms, not the content, to satisfy their confused senses and needs for meaning. Less is more — even though they pretend otherwise, all this is compensation. You have to learn to read beyond words and forms, only through voice intonation and body language. Everything reveals our balance or imbalance of the impulses of life and death, reflected in our feminine and masculine proportions that enables or hinders us to balance our love/hate equation.

"The veil has become a double-edged sword used by the man to exhibit his ownership over the woman; at the same time the conditioned woman has adapted to it and is now using to protect herself against the coarse, uncultured and unrestrained libido of men in the Middle East where the public place is disorganized and unprotected. It primarily functions as a defense from intimidation and the so called 'evil-eye' in a very superstitious environment.

"Where the subtle science of proxemics is respected there is no need for this flagrant physical subtraction tool. The woman wearing a veil is either hiding her beauty or ugliness, neither developing her true nor fake self or persona, but reducing herself to a ghost-like, soulless object behind a curtain. It's similar to living permanently under a walking tent. In the West, wearing the veil or hijab has also become a subliminal political message of anti-democracy, anti-Western values, stating, '*I am against women's equality, your freedoms and democracy.*' The woman assuming this role is a textbook Stockholm syndrome victim conditioned by men experts in rhetoric, deception, manipulation and conspiracy theories.

"The veil might also have a fetishist element for insecure and immature men to feel manlier if women look inferior and submissive. If a woman likes sex, she is branded a 'nymphomaniac', but if a man does, he is considered a 'man'. But unless a man finds a woman who is free and likes sex as much as he does, he would have to do with another man, and thus be branded a homosexual. Some men are weak and want to reduce the woman's role to someone who is submissive and would spend her entire time at home or under a cloak to hedge against the vagaries and failures of seduction, while he has the liberties of doing what he wishes for. Man comes from the womb, and spends his entire life searching for a way to get back into it."

"But I read that there is no such rule anywhere in religious books about this veil, Gaia; that it is just a political tool, as you said, to confuse and exasperate the West and its values."

"We look for extra-terrestrial life in Space but are unable to communicate peacefully with each other or other species sharing our own planet. Who says we will understand and get along with other forms of intelligence from other galaxies?

"The alienation from life is relative to the promises made by religions. Any promises, hopes or 'faith', as religions call it Mario, has the power to disconnect the individual from life's reality and make him live in denial and expectancy. In a bid to compete against each other and bring more followers, each subsequent religion has raised the stakes for offers and promises in the afterlife, thus alienating people from genuine life responsibilities. While Moses introduced the Ten Commandments as a purely ethical system to manage and resolve the social problems of his time, he did not say much about the afterlife besides that we shall be rewarded according to our actions. In the Old Testament it is implied that after death, man returns *'ashes to ashes, dust to dust'*. Furthermore, promises made by Jewish eschatology are concerned only with the events that shall happen in the *'End of days'*, namely the gathering of the Jewish people, the return of the Messiah to guide them and the revival of the dead. Therefore beliefs in an afterlife are not imprinted in the Jewish mind as they are in the modern Christian or Islamic sense. In the *New Testament*, the afterlife is never described in detail, although most post-Jesus Christians believe that after death a person is rewarded with eternal life or eternal damnation, in the presence of a God or some kind of a portrayed red devil. The only thing mentioned for sure is that the soul of each individual separates from the body at death to be reunited at the resurrection.

"Around AD 600 came the creed of Islam which raised the stakes of an afterlife even higher, stating that this life is merely a preparation for the passage to the afterlife. It also compartmentalized paradise to different levels, and in order to access the highest and seventh, the Muslim has to die in the name of God.

"According to Muslim eschatology, everything that a person longs to do in this life is in Jannah, or paradise, and it offers significant details about this paradise. One day in paradise is considered equal to a thousand years on earth. Palaces are made from bricks of gold, silver and pearls. Traditions note the presence of horses and camels of dazzling whiteness, large trees, and mountains made of musk between which rivers flow in valleys of pearl and ruby. It is also said there are rivers of milk, of which the taste never changes, rivers of wine, delicious to those who drink it, and rivers of clarified honey. [14]

"Every person's life runs on a program. It might be Greek, Celtic, Nordic, Hindu, African mythology or simply secular humanism. But if the CBOS is monotheistic religion run for your life, religion has become a dysfunction, ingratitude and rejection of the gift of life in all its splendor and generosity; a collective existential sickness for immature, emotionally inclined white-haired children looking for a parental authority figure to alleviate the fear of death. Whoever lives in the past or expectation is not ready. Life is a paradox and antagonists are complementary. Truth, beauty and love stand on a very fine line in the middle.

"We spend our lives putting order to our minds, assembling our ideas into beliefs to create a reality in which to interact with others, just to end up identifying with those beliefs interpreting them as divine. If we don't get rid of these convictions, preconceived beliefs, judgments and ideas we won't be able to perceive and appreciate life as it is, in its pure essence."

"According to the scriptures, God spoke only three times to his messengers. Why doesn't he speak to us anymore? Do you think he's upset or angry at us, Gaia?"

"Ha-ha-ha-ha. No, but this is the intrigue, the Catch 22." She winked. "When someone stays alone for so long, secluded on a mountain or down a valley, you can be sure he will start hearing voices in his head and see visions with his blurred eyes. The scourge of religion is spiritual greed: everyone wants more than life, and they clash and disagree on the interior design of this paradise and afterlife. Every religion depicts it in different scenery, a different setting. This is why it was dubbed opium and collective neurosis."

"What exactly is Karma?"

"It is the cosmic balance sheet concealed in your subconscious mind and carved in your DNA. God doesn't want the ignorant fool, who did not do his homework for self-discovery and regained his free will, to find it easily. And because people are lazy and short-sighted they go for ready-to-adopt, ready-to-consume religion for instant gratification.

"We enter life from the womb and exit it through the tomb, and both are mothers. There is a direct link between men's rule, subjectivity and emotional dependency; patriarchal authority and religious societies project a certain family model deficient in the feminine element. The kingdoms of heaven are open for those who do not kill or interrupt the cycle of life, but cherish and respect it. Understand that death is a longer sleep in the natural cycle of life.

"The watch in your hand, Mario, ticks to the seconds, minutes and hours. The clock of life ticks to the years, decades and centuries. This is Karma. Some say the stars in the skies are the souls of people who have died. Religion has alienated people and disconnected them from nature, real life, and understanding. If you reconcile people with death, you heal the world."

Suddenly I noticed time had flown by and we'd been talking for hours on end. The last remaining customers were paying the cashier, while the rest of the staff were busy dimming the lights and lowering the bookstore shutters. I thought these had been the most important hours of my life.

"It is getting late Gaia. Would you like to go for a dinner together?"

"With pleasure, Mario. If we can find a vegetarian place at this time."

"I can think of one. Do you mind taking the motorbike?"

As we walked to the parking lot and bestrode the seats, she laced her arms around me. I turned the engine on, tightened the clutch and released it toward the highway's entrance ramp, as dusk was master of the ceremony.

6. 9/11/2001

Once, on a cross-country flight from Montgomery County Airpark, Gaithersburg, MD to Vermont's Burlington International Airport for the purpose of accumulating flying time towards my Commercial Pilot License, I was overflying Newburgh Town, NY's Class D airspace. According to my map I was fifty nautical miles west of New York City and my tanks, which I had just topped off at Stewart's Airport, had plenty of fuel for the rest of the journey. I could already perceive, far in the horizon, the imposing high-rise buildings and the legendary buzz that characterizes Manhattan, with its lively streets and intersecting highways.

Having heard of an approved sightseeing tour overflying the Hudson River, I radioed a request to the airspace controller while I was still in uncontrolled territory in order to get clearance for Class C and B airways. The request was declined, stating traffic congestion and overload. Nonetheless, realizing this was a unique opportunity, I kept circling on the edge of the airspace, bidding another request thirty minutes later, when radio silence followed. My persistence paid off, though, as the second time permission was granted.

Following the controller's vectors and discretionary advice, I navigated the Cessna 172 toward the river, taking into consideration the reported wind speed and direction. As the distance grew less, my breathing and my heart rate accelerated; it felt like a fantasy woven and made possible by all the dedicated time, effort, mind order, and regulations to produce this level of organization and team work — an ultimate feat of civilization.

I was over the Hudson, engaging its narrow corridor, when the controller released me in VFR (Visual Flying Rules), bidding me, *"Keep a watchful eye for other traffic and enjoy the tour,"* with discernible amusement in his voice.

The experience was mindboggling and enchanting, similar to a dream after which, upon waking up, one's life is completely altered. Sharing this space and energy with all the other airplanes and helicopters in this self-organizing bustle was an ultimate pattern of synchronism; being part of the tiny yet indispensable components of collective living.

Later that same year, in July 1999, John F. Kennedy, Jr. was on a Night VFR flight from New York to Massachusetts with his wife and sister-in-law when their aircraft crashed in a very unfortunate and tragic air traffic accident into the Atlantic Ocean, across

Martha's Vineyard. The NTSB report concluded loss of control caused by spatial disorientation.

I had accumulated forty-five hours and three thousand nautical miles on that journey, including engine checks, taxiing and stop-overs. But most importantly, my mindset was consolidated forever in the third dimension. We live most of the time in a two-dimensional world with the coordinates of distance and time, for which we think speed, is the third. Altitude was the added dimension.

* * *

And yet in 2001, some people found a way to direct their hatred and animosity toward this symbol of modern multi-ethnic realization. New York City became the stage for a terrorist act because it is the forefront of Western civilization, as well as for having the word 'New' and the 'Lady Liberty' as an archetype, which taunt any foe of freedom, change and gender equality — things sclerotic minds dread.

On the political front, as usual, propaganda, misinformation and conspiracy theories swarmed in endless blame games, mixed messages and justifications to blur the truth and sow confusion. The United States of America was the first nation to be edified in various cultures as well as to have addressed discrimination, offering equal opportunities to all people of the planet. And while some point to two events in its history such as the American Indian Wars and the use of the atomic bomb in WWII to counter an imminent threat and save the world from doom and ruthless tyrants, let them first examine their own countries' history books and see where they stand today with regards to their past. Have they evolved or backpedalled? There is no history without trouble and people in glass houses should not throw stones. All these accusations and guilt trips/blame games are textbook reverse psychology cases and collective Dramatic Triangles.

Some cultures are chronically incompatible with freedoms and democracy. This all stems from a family model favoring an archaic father figure for the sake of maintaining a dysfunctional disorderly society by keeping emotions inflamed, and exalting the egos and feeling of self-importance through existentialism, nostalgia and melancholy. People coming from repressive governments are familiar with being followers of cults of the personality. They need a father figure in the political and religious arenas to replace the unbalanced rigid parental authority, and criticize the West because they are incapable of appreciating simple subtle freedoms such as free thoughts and expression. They confuse socialism with communism and democracy with anarchy, taking for granted the things they aren't discriminated or persecuted for. They hoped for total liberty of action in a highly emotional environment for their animated gesticulations and articulations to maintain their skewed proxemics and body language. I wonder where Michael Moore or Noam Chomsky would be today had they lived in another country. Would they still be alive or rotting in a jail, yearning for a taste of water and a sunray?

We live in a delicate world of antagonism. While Capitalism is synonymous with hedonism and is a byproduct of excessive production, consumerism and democracy; Communism on the other hand is repression and inhibition of basic freedoms and human rights, frustration, abuse and misinterpretation of socialism that sacrificed the free human will and spirit in exchange for a bottle of vodka and a loaf of bread, in another form of parental authority where the ruler or the ruling party replaces the Almighty and the clerics. Any system that rules by repression, fear and excessive authority will produce cult of the personality cohorts and immature neurotic individuals.

It was said that globalization was the Americanization of the world, while it turned out to be its 'China-zation'. With the fall of the ex-USSR, everybody anticipated a Russian and Chinese smooth transition towards democracy. What emerged instead was the worst of two systems: Communist Capitalism.

We owe it to Mother Earth, if not to future generations, to bridge the gap between these conflicting ideologies to save the human soul and this precious nurturing planet.

PART III

7. Financial Markets

Bailey's Gym, Los Angeles, California — 6am — the fall of 1999. I was visiting my old buddy Elrob with whom I had lost touch for many years after he decided to dedicate his time for the motion picture industry and I for aviation.

It was still dawn when the sound system started broadcasting those strange lines about enjoying the power and beauty of our youth, not worrying about the future and never-mind getting married or divorced at forty. What the hell was that? I interrupted my training to listen more carefully. What were those lines and who was conferring those words of wisdom on that morning? Every word sliced through my mind like a sharp sword, shaking my thoughts, stirring my perception.

Later on that day I asked Elrob if he'd heard of any new tune that boasted these lyrics, but he answered negatively. It took many months for the song to become popular on the airwaves and discover its title, "*Everybody's Free to Wear Sunscreen*" by Baz Luhrmann. And after so many years, it didn't lose its magic and I still listen to it frequently to remind myself of the timeless wisdom we shelter ourselves from, trying to live in denial from sheer reality.

What was strange about California was that every time I visited, a new pursuit kicked off in my life. There must have been some kind of relation between the beauty of its land and the yearning for discovery. It was also a time that gold jumped thirty percent while oil tumbled and I had made a small fortune, attributed to pure beginner's luck, by holding positions for both in the right direction.

My interest was beginning to veer toward financial markets, particularly a new discipline that was gaining popularity among market aficionados, but it still had to consolidate its marks and prove its efficiency. Literature was scarce about it, so one had to search in order to find and discover more, and that was a challenge I longed for.

8.   A Tale from a Coffee Shop

It all started on a winter's afternoon. It was raining cats and dogs outside. The wind was gusting with bursts of hail, while thunder and lightning were splitting the skies, unleashing nature's wrath as it was believed a long time ago. I was lucky to have made it to that neon sign advertising my favorite American-style café un-soaked, while my umbrella had been torn to pieces by the might of the wind as I was walking swiftly along the city's wall, sheltering from the havoc above.

From my traveling backpack, I unpacked my two laptops and cell phone, through which I entered and exited the markets. My computers were booted and ready to go as the raindrops were building a wall of haze on the windowpanes, drawing sketches that were leaving the visitors reflective when I noticed a man sitting across the place, scrutinizing me with a smile.

"Hello, I am Mario," I pitched at him.

"Well, hello, Mario. You can call me Pythagoras," he answered.

"Pythagoras! You must be Greek, then," I hit back with a playful wink.

"Let's just say I come from a long lineage of Greek descendants," he replied, with a twist in his voice. "And you are ... an itinerant trader?"

Something in my mind clicked. My intuition was pointing to something familiar, some kind of *déjà-vu*. It might have been his features or physiognomy, but my memory was telling me otherwise.

"How did you guess?" I reacted, trying to hide my surprise.

"From your books." He pointed his finger at the new books I had just purchased from the local bookstore: *The Profit Magic of Stock Transaction Timing* by J. M. Hurst, and Martin Pring's *Trading Systems Explained*.

"Yes, indeed. Everywhere and nowhere are my homes, and that's the beauty of this craft: it procures total freedom and independence for whosoever is willing to walk the talk."

It was at that time I had just made then lost 140 grand in stocks, trading information such as Price/Earnings ratio, Price Earnings to Growth ratio, income statements, balance sheets, and 52 week highs and lows from financial sections of popular websites. I'd thought the market was a generous benefactor and that whoever had a few dollars to lend could take it back fructified and multiplied at least two or threefold. Having since discovered the ruthless, unforgiving nature of the markets, and coming from a context of fighting sports, I had made a new resolution: to discover everything I could about my newly encountered foe and learn to dance its dance, no matter the cost or time.

"So how is the market treating you nowadays?" he asked.

"Well, you know what they say," I retorted with a little nervous tic in my face, as if revealing my secret. "Sometimes you win, sometimes you lose, sometimes you laugh, sometimes you cry."

"Hmm, that sounds as if it is a fifty-fifty strive. I thought you wanted to make a living from the markets. How can you survive if there is such a high element of chance?" He went on, "Can I ask you a personal question?"

"Sure, go ahead!" I thought in my mind; *Huh, make my day, whoever you think you are.*

"Why do you trade? Why did you pick this challenging and unpredictable craft?"

"Well, as I told you! It procures independence and freedom."

"While this is in part true, it is only the surface of it. What draws us to the market is collective psychology. We know without knowing that there is something in that market beyond the financial and material gains and losses, and then there are the fears of being excluded and that of missing out. There are three kinds of people attracted to it: the gamblers, the materialists and spiritualists. This whole world is driven by an existential question, the eternal search for meanings in an endless loop of simulation and stimulation. So, which kind are you?"

I could hear my heartbeat. Holy moly, I thought, is this guy for real or out of some kind of fiction? And his name! Must be for something; either given or earned.

"So what do we do," I snapped back, "in the face of this eternal unsolvable and ungraspable search or quest, as you call it?"

"As a market participant, Mario, you have to transcend, tame your ego. I don't know how much experience you have in this field, but the most important aspect in life, and trading in particular, is of psychological and spiritual dimensions. No one will succeed in the long run if not in tune and harmony with universal laws. Let's have tea. How do you like your drink?"

"Never mind, I'll get them. How would you like yours?"

As I returned from the bar carrying two cups of steaming tea, he was flipping through the pages of my books. As soon as he held the cup in his hand, he took a sip from it and followed, "Contrary to what many believe, Technical Analysis is an ancient discipline. Long before Elliott, Da Vinci, and Fibonacci, there was a Greek philosopher mathematician who discovered the magic of squares and numbers, Golden Proportions, and founded a religion based on nature's laws and metempsychosis: day and night; awakening and sleep; being fractals in the bigger cycle of life and death.

"In today's world, running at the speed of light, Fundamental Analysis has become obsolete. You need Technical Analysis to keep up with the new pace of the paradigm shifts and dynamic changes that have occurred since the telecommunication revolution. Fundamental analysts are like existentialists, spending their time looking for the 'why' of things, while technical analysts are concerned with the 'how': how to enter and exit the market. Technical Analysis is a more accurate and leading discipline. The chart is your treasure map; follow the chart."

He put the books down. I felt as if time was suspended.

"What you are reading is very bright; however, you need to add to it a metaphysical measure of ethical dimension. Otherwise your endeavor will be devoid and dull in this vast and infinite universe."

"And how do I add this measure?" I asked, dumbfounded.

"All our fears are those of mortals, yet our desires of immortals," he followed on. "Beauty is proportion and moderation. People attribute different names to the same principles, trying to interpret them in an infinite variety of ways, creating conflict and misunderstanding. If we observe this world, nature, and the universe, we cannot miss underlying active laws from which everything is inspired, namely the Law of Karma, from which the Golden Rule came '*The Principle of Consensual Reciprocity*'. Technical Analysis can show you this way.

"Through the ages, mystics, philosophers, gurus,

so-called messengers and prophets fasted, mused, searched, and came up with systems of beliefs, what they called truths, to live and achieve self-realization and fulfillment in this world. From Egypt to Greece, India, China, Japan, North and South America, they dwelled hard and proposed for us 'The Ways'. From the principles of Hermeticism, Kama Sutraism, Poly- to Monotheism, Communism to Capitalism, left or right, success and happiness, pleasure or pain, love or hate...There is so much wisdom in this world, yet people choose evil out of ignorance, chauvinism, dogmatism, narrow-mindedness, and ideologies.

"But what is the merit of a monk, rabbi, priest, sheikh, or prophet who finds the truth when isolated on a mountain top, in a desert, or down a valley when he then comes to the city to herald it as the ultimate truth if he was unable to find it in the first place among his people, amid the daily businesses, concerns and preoccupations of life in the city? And why would he veil it in some secret cryptic message, riddle, or mystery if his true intention is to benefit all humankind? It might be that the truth is simple, yet to conceal and complicate it he would draw and seduce the weak, curious, and discontent in life and bring some attention to himself and his philosophy.

"You trade instruments in the market and roles in life, but the ultimate commodity is love. Not the kind of exclusive, romantic, possessive love experienced between two individuals which nourishes our ego, safeguards our pool of genes on the narcissistic level and organizes society. But rather the type of love that binds us all, without self-interest, to creation and the entire human family. It is experienced as compassion, oneness and empathy. Everything else is a replacement; every excess is compensation.

"There is an ongoing battle waged in the stock market. Every support, resistance and trend-line are frontlines where buyers and sellers confront, this whole economic system is dependent on a vicious cycle of production, consumption and a barrel of oil among competing nations. There is an analogy between trading and martial arts: today's traders are modern warriors and modern samurais. You need to be prepared for it technically, psychologically and financially. Whenever you are successful, give back a share of what you have been rewarded and never trade above the means of your retribution. The cardinal sin in life and trading is pride; the only conviction worth having is having no convictions. You have to accept and embrace uncertainty. Having convictions closes your senses, blurs your perception, and makes you biased in life. All you need is the Golden Rule and the Golden Number. But most importantly," he said, "Never lose your head. The measure of a man is inversely proportional to the size of his ego."

On that day there was a Golden Number, a Golden Rule, a Gold Trade, and the never-ending flow of time. I had made ten grand setting up a Fibonacci level, confirmed by all the signals of the MACD (Moving Average Convergence-Divergence) with a 1:3 risk/reward ratio, but most importantly, I had opened my eyes to a new dimension…

* * *

The following months, I totally committed myself to a new journey. I knew where it would start, but never suspected where it would lead or what I would discover. The encounter with the person calling himself 'Pythagoras' had a major impact on the course of my life. It was no coincidence; what Gaia would have called synchronicity. The man gave me hints at a most critical time and pointed me in new directions to tackle the markets and life in general. I was now devoted to investigating further, developing and improving what I had previously learned but on a different level and with a different approach, in a rather spiritual manner.

A quick search on the internet and renewed visits to Barnes & Noble yielded some very interesting material on the subject, and I needed time and a sanctuary to cogitate the next steps to undertake. So I packed my backpack, filled my tank and hit the road toward my favorite coffee joint in the middle of nowhere.

9. Philanthropy and the Art of Technical Analysis

It was dark outside. As I looked into the vast starry sky, the mist of my hot chocolate drawing forms into the night, a shooting star passed far above...was it a fast traveling soul or an extinguished one, liberated from the bondage of earthly life? Drawn into my thoughts and contemplating questions about life's relative purpose and finiteness within the infinite universe, I wondered: was it all predetermined, planned or random? Is there such a thing as free will or are we unconsciously guided and misguided in our lives? Are we responsible or irresponsible for our thoughts, words and deeds? Does universal justice exist and prevail beyond the partial and subjective human one? So many questions that have driven the human spirit, sometimes to great achievements and realizations, at other times to disillusionment, misery, atrocities, self-consumption and self-destruction...

I remember when I was a child, life was much

simpler. We were kind of in heaven before the fall from grace; all we had to do was eat, sleep and play. Now we eat, sleep and pray: pray for our creator to forgive our sins, to preserve our soul, to make us happy, healthy and rich. But what makes something good or bad, and does the Dude upstairs really interfere in human affairs? Does He or She have managers and directors to run the daily chores of life or does everything run on automatic pilot, some kind of a Divine Formula, a Divine Algorithm? It was a sort of a mono-chat I had with the Tenant of the Blue Tent, an insightful conversation from that café in the middle of nowhere.

The tape was playing the latest prices on the Bloomberg channel; the hosts of the program were entertaining their audience by offering motives and justifications for the latest price movements. The quotes on my portable computer were flickering green and red. I was waiting for predetermined price levels to trigger my trades and I was smiling, because my newly applied discipline was able to protect me from all the bullish and bearish nonsense on TV.

I've always been like this: a rebel who wouldn't settle for anything less than that which would steal his heart away. Motorcycles did it, flying and aviation, natural beauty from inside and out, sincere people, pragmatic not sterile philosophy and Technical Analysis. If anything, the Stock Market teaches us mostly about ourselves, the famous Delphic Oracle: true lessons in modesty, temperance, humility and the interconnectedness of things, either on the investing, trading or speculative sides. The graph with its tools of lines, angles, retracements and indicators reveals for us the way within the various cycles of finance and the global economy, probing them when healthy and strong, exposing them when weak and failing.

The beauty of it all was that for the orderly and wise, this applies in all spheres of life, if one was willing to look beyond the apparent noise and bustle of things. It was the manifestation and representation in one graph of all the states of human affairs, the heartbeat of this world.

Oil prices had been rising for quite some time now, shooting to levels unseen in the past, into uncharted territory, reflecting the turmoil and unrest from the Middle East, a region plagued by too many myths, history, conflicts and claims of exclusivity in God, land and religion; an irrational volatility pattern in human behavior only measured by some invisible Bollinger Bands. But whenever this kind of conduct departed from common sense, taking a steeper trend-line and direction, after many trials and errors, hopes and regrets, and after it has caused all the havoc and pain, misery and suffering, and gone from one extreme to another reflected in the most accurate oscillator, sooner or later it will eventually find its way back to reason: some kind of a Moving Average, a Standard Deviation Channel or the 45-degrees Gann Angle.

Events in life have always been like this, best embodied in the beautiful lyrics of the song "*Windmills of Your Mind*" written by Alan and Marilyn Bergman; like circles in spirals, like wheels within wheels.

An indiscernible ripple, wave or tide somehow, somewhere, always at play, always in action...

Unfortunately this shall be the state of our world as long as we encourage the culture of being slaves to our own disproportional material and spiritual greed, fears, hopes and expectations. Karmic Law playing the regulator in it all, some sort of a Divine Algorithm: a universal calculator for our cosmic balance sheet.

We are always tempted by instant gratification instead of a delayed one, but whenever we choose the first over of the second, sooner or later we will pay a price. It goes the same when we look after our own personal interest at the expenses of the community and others.

"*Whatever goes around, comes around;*" many great minds, philosophers and so-called prophets and messengers observed this and wrote about it extensively, each in their own way. Corollaries are many; the oldest and most legendary one was eternalized in Antiquity's Golden Rule, and reiterated by Confucius, Buddha and Jesus:

"Do not do to others what you do not want them to do to you";

"Hurt not others in ways that you yourself would find hurtful";

"Treat others the way you would like to be treated".

But Hinduism also had its own in the famous Namaste salute: "*The divine particle in me salutes the divine particle in you*", which literarily implies reducing one's ego in the presence of one another. Socrates could have never said enough about it in his eternal quest for ethics and justice, and later Rousseau and the necessity for a Social Contract and conventions. Emanuel Kant as well introduced imperatives to his philosophy: *"Treat others not as a means, but as an end"*. And if we add to the list Newton's Third Law of Motion, Lavoisier's Theory of Mass Conservation and Murphy's Law, we get a menu for rules and principles all generated and inspired by the Rule of Karma: an irrefutable principle of cause and effect; an inescapable unbendable cosmic law that, together with the love of giving, is the founding principle of this life.

From Ancient Greek comes the word *Philos*, which means friend, and *Anthropos*, for human. Philanthropy translates into friend of humans, love for others; a precursory name for Humanism. Our ancient Greek friends also distinguished four types of love:

- Eros for romance
- Storge for affection
- Philia for friendship
- And Agape for unconditional love

While the apparent forms of philanthropy seem to be similar, their motivation might vary: to reduce taxes, to obtain others' acknowledgment, to show off as a benefactor, but there also exists a genuine motive based on compassion, empathy and the ultimate realization that everything is one. Having a conscience and oneness are the same. We're all concerned and affected by everything in this interwoven world and more so today than any other time in human history: *"A butterfly flap of wings in Brazil might cause a cyclone in China and a mosquito bite in Africa can spread the disease to the U.S. and Russia"*.

Irrespective of our words and deeds, intention is what counts; what life holds us accountable for. Even though many a creed or act seems nice and altruistic at first glance, it can be motivated by these two incentives: having others' acknowledgment; and wanting to show off as benefactors. In the long run, we are what we think and do; in the short run, we are what we intend. Intention and free will guide our future and destiny. Are we driven by self-interest or detachment from ourselves and consideration for others?

No thought, intention or deed goes unaccountable. Not in the organized, conspicuous religious logic, but in the universal one measured only by empathy and compassion. In life we ought to pay some toll back, the way we responsibly pay our taxman.

Technical Analysis wasn't only portending to financial markets, it was beginning to teach me the middle way. It was, I discovered, a gauging instrument to be used in various fields and provinces.

Sometimes we know without knowing deep inside each one of us that everything is one; that we reap what we sow, yet we try to ignore it. All is well carved in our genes and subconscious minds; some have called it conscience, philosophers have mused about it for mental gymnastics, and religions have exploited it for mass control and manipulation. Few people have adopted it as higher values and principles in their lives: life as breathing and sharing according to the Karmic Law and the School of Life.

My cup had been empty for a while without noticing, as I was absorbed in the beauty of the sky. There was no one left in the coffee shop except the bartender tidying up her stuff and getting ready to leave. As I was emerging from my contemplation, a reminiscence from schooldays flashed back at me — a quote from my favorite philosopher, Voltaire: *"The world intrigues me, and I cannot think that this clock is ticking and has no watchmaker."*

And I thought, God exists, but not the way they tell us about...

10. The Merits and Hazards of Technical Analysis

After many months immersed in business books, I had learned a great deal on the topic at hand; although compared to the boundless available information, I was still a novice. One thing, however, became immediately obvious; that from the study of financial markets arose two schools of thought: one that considers numbers; the other charts. While the ongoing debate about the competence and efficiency of each in market timing and forecasting continued to draw more ink on paper, it looked rather like a conundrum. As it might be that the two modes of living lurking in people's minds affected their choices in life and inclined them toward one method or the other.

Fundamental analysts enjoyed crunching figures, numbers and dwelling on meanings, explanations and interpretations. Technical analysts, on the other hand, only concern themselves with the best time and levels to enter and exit the market, employing tools of surgical precision.

To enter the crux of the matter, let us first define what Technical Analysis claims to be. In a technician's words, *"It is the study of market action (price, volume, and open interest) for the purpose of forecasting future price trends"*.

Technicians derive three premises for the establishment of their discipline:

- Market action discounts everything

- Prices move in trends

- History repeats itself [15]

Every premise, once accepted, paves the way for applying the next until the three are fulfilled.

In a world running at the speed of light, the speed of wavelengths' travel and ideas, the need for a discipline that provides both dynamism and interactivity with the market is crucial. Since the inception of the internet, the media and telecom revolutions, online brokerage leveraged accounts fitted onto video-game-style platforms, with infinite market participants coming from various cultural and disciplinary backgrounds, the personality, anatomy and rhythm of the market have changed. A buy and hold strategy would simply mean living the infernal cycle of greed, fear, hopes, and regrets. Although Fundamental Analysis might be good to determine the glitches in an economy, it has become too static and obsolete for short and medium term trading. If price action is based on supply and demand then the study of the price, which is the main skill of the technician, involves the underlying fundamental forces that move that market.

Every instrument and every market has a unique personality that collectively reflects that of its participants: certain trends and patterns, despite having different appearances and cycles, show consistency. When academics argue the heresy and inefficacy of Technical Analysis in the Random Walk or Efficient Market Theories, they contradict themselves. For when they say it is too subjective to be efficient and then add that it is a self-fulfilling prophecy, that everyone acting in concert using Technical Analysis creates these trends and patterns, they prove themselves wrong. For how can it be too subjective and make people act in concert at the same time? They simply lack the experience and foresight in that market. If the market is a reflection of the collective psychology of its participants, then it must have a collective personality — and every personality is subject to recurrent behaviors and attitudes, study and classification, qualitative and quantitative analysis.

Another pointless critique by Technical Analysis detractors is that the past cannot predict the future. Mind you, any science, descriptive or inductive, relies on past experiments and data dissemination for the establishment of its foundation. If Fundamental Analysis can still be good for long-term investment, it cannot survive the dire need for timing in the derivatives market beside the advantages offered by Technical Analysis: versatility; flexibility; and adaptability to different instruments and timeframes.

And so the next question: is Technical Analysis a science or an art? It might be both, and that's the beauty, as the limit which separates the two is often thin. Since any art is the expression and representation of life, it would be more appropriate to think of it perhaps as a scientific art or an artful science that provides us with a safety net, to gauge and plan this fast-moving and fast-changing market. Similar to encephalograms, cardiograms or seismographs experts use in other disciplines.

More than ever, today's markets are the reflection of the states of all human affairs: political; economic; social; and ecological, depicted on a day-to-day, week-to-week, and monthly graphs. If we drew a random line across a chart and committed to buying every time the price broke up and selling every time the price broke down, we would have made money, or at least not lost any. So what if that line had any indication based on mathematical formulas and geometrical figures to point out the strengths and weaknesses of that market? This is what Technical Analysis is all about.

It might be worth adding that any discipline which can be taught to virtually anyone has no guarantee of success and has its own rate of successes or failures, of winners and losers. In any particular profession, how many would end up among the best? It has been said that only three to five percent survive, the rest are here just for the fun and thrill of it: Darwin's Law at play. Thus is the condition of this world, and of the markets.

* * *

I had just finished presenting a Certified Financial Technician exam and was heading back home from that busy airport. It had been a while now since this quest started: years of study, experiments, and sleepless nights.

It was a hell of a journey of self-discovery, of money lost and found and knowledge about the dynamics that move our world. But who ever said that fortune comes overnight or that providence opens its door to the first comer? The preparation of a trader is similar to the preparation of a fighter. It necessitates physical and psychological prowess, wisdom and humility. It takes many attributes to succeed in life.

There were many lessons to be learned from the trading and investment floors: that the chart is the heartbeat of this world; that there are identifiable trends and patterns among people visible in finance; that human behavior, though unpredictable, is often recurrent. But also, that trading and investing is a three-legged stool: strategy; psychology; and risk management.

Academics were just beginning to acknowledge the efficiency of Technical Analysis through the development of Behavioral Finance by studying correlations between psychology and the economy, and I knew something was missing in my preparation.

The voice on the public address system was announcing the next boarding, and I had some time to kill before my flight. Having studied aviation, I always felt charmed by airports, and had somehow quite comprehended what Saint-Exupéry meant in his comparison of the airplane window as the looking glass of the planet. From that angle and some altitude is one able to realize the futility of many things in life: all this hustle and bustle underneath, all this activity in search of something undefinable, ungraspable, that may or may not be. People traveling through airport hubs and gates go through a reality-check without noticing.

Every culture has its own values, rituals, traditions and paradigms that set up a matrix for its own reality. And whoever is transiting from one country to another, experiences with or without being aware, a shift of perception that can be beneficial and enriching or detrimental and destructive to his self-constructed ego and identity, if one is unwilling to submit to explicit and implicit self-questioning.

The bookshelves at the airport duty-free shop were appealing, each cover promising a new adventure. I remember being taught there are three approaches to the financial world: gambling, materialism, and spirituality. Each group held its own views on the markets according to fostered biases and expectations. The stock market is the biggest test and teacher of all, mostly in lessons of greed, fear, hopes and regrets with their inescapable consequences. All these emotions run parallel to our basic instincts, the impulses of life and death. One book in the business section caught my attention, *The Buddhist Trader* by Mercedes Oestermann Van Essen. While I was flipping through its pages, I realized its benefits to supplement my education.

The cashier was in her mid-thirties, natural and very well-mannered; her smile also revealed soft eyes reflecting goodness in life. Once the book had been paid for, I found a quiet place in the airport lounge and started reading.

The table of contents presented subjects rarely encountered in investment literature, a very well-structured course in trading psychology. Clearly and concisely written lessons as well as practical examples demonstrated how our conditioning generates and validates our preferences. How it affects our trading, and how we should overcome the need to be right all the time to unlock this self-defeating behavior deeply rooted in our subconscious. How to tame compulsive habits every time we face the same situations; how to embrace and accept uncertainty, discipline ourselves, stop blaming others, the markets or some conspiracy theory for our failures and disappointments, and how to make sound decisions and assume responsibility. Finally, there were techniques and exercises for staying in the quiet zone. By dissecting the human psyche, the author offered methods for calming the mind and taming the ego.

There is a discrepancy in our minds between what should happen and what actually occurs in the real world, and this is the essential difference between technical and other forms of analysis. In trading, one must learn to overcome all biases and ego trips by embracing neutrality with the highest degree of humility to achieve serenity, which is the most difficult part of trading. What separates the realists from the optimists and pessimists could only be done by developing a detached and objective eye upon the world. The book also reminded me of the marvelous worlds of Zen and Buddhism I had visited a while ago at the library. By linking them to the financial world, this book yielded immense benefits on the trading as well as the personal development side and the apprehension of higher realms of reality.

The plane was ready to board, with people moving around the lounge as if something was missing. We all live in a psychosomatic world: a world of ideas; beliefs; projections; and perceptions. I was grateful to providence for putting that book on my path that day, as well to Mercedes Oestermann Van Essen for her honesty and generosity which put the crowning jewel in the preparation of the very special craft we aspire to.

11. Greed and Fear

The subject of greed and fear is all too important in life and financial markets in particular. In order to tackle it, we first ought to define a few concepts. What are human emotions, and what are their incidence and impact on our daily interactions?

All our actions are governed by our emotions. At the far ends of the collection of emotions lie two major one: greed and fear. Those two emotions run parallel to the impulses of life and death, better known in Freudian terminology as *Libido* and *Mortido*.

When we see the ticks of the underlying security we are trying to buy or sell go up or down on our screens, so do our heartbeats. But are we going to let our emotions take control or are we going to reign over them? There resides the difference between winning or losing in the stock market. Once we step into the investing arena we are in a dangerous environment, and going there unprepared is like facing a wild animal — a bear or a bull, as a matter of fact. If we don't get to know that animal and tame it, it will maim us.

Greed is nothing but excessive desire. Fear is the exact opposite force, and both are born from unreasonable, immoderate expectations.

When we undertake a new activity we all start with disproportional dreams and expectations. But like the neophyte, when asked to stage his first fight is crippled and overtaken by cold hands and feet when he steps onto a martial arts mat; so shall we experience the same fate when the investment we just engaged in starts going in the opposite direction. If we didn't train hard and study even harder, in the instance of trading, to increase, perfect and hone our knowledge, passing many tests by trial and error while diligently drawing from our lessons tactics and strategies, we would never have made it to being good fighters, traders or investors, never mind champions or would-be millionaires.

And so, where do we start and how to proceed?

First, it is very important to acknowledge that trading is not a game, nor an endeavor for the faint-hearted. Trading is a very serious business, and getting into the worlds of trading and investments requires many imperatives and prerequisites, among them knowledge, patience, self-control and ascetic risk and money management. No method of trading or investing is a hundred percent foolproof; the best probabilities befall between fifty and seventy percent, but so are most things in life.

The financial market is by far the most challenging test in discipline and decision making. Yet this ruthless and amazing teacher is here to always keep us on our toes, our senses wide open, learning and constantly evolving.

12. The Divine Proportions

A light breeze was carrying the fresh fragrance of newly opened spring buds floating in the air as if to tickle the olfactory senses, awakening them to the simple beauty and pleasures of life while the sun was settling down across the horizon, reminding us of another day gone by, another page turned in our personal history. As I strolled down the narrow streets and alleys of the city's center, a map in my hands, looking for a quiet place to disengage, I couldn't stop pondering, being the technical analyst I am and having acquired the second nature that comes with it: the little details, subtle things along my way that are indicative and predictive of certain meanings and values and precursors of coming changes; some sort of crowd psychology.

Every city has its own story, history, and architecture revealing a lot about the people who inhabit it, reflecting the neuronal order or chaos, organization or disorganization that sprang up and settled in their minds a long time ago due to the myths, legends and tales they adopted as their collective archetypes, and consequently founded their religion, culture, and civilization. Like the financial chart on my screens, the map in my hand was yielding a treasure trove of information, whether from a geographic, demographic or social perspective.

As I ushered open the door, the atmosphere was warm and serene in that coffee shop, which offered comfortable couches and pleasant music. The speakers were filling the space with the deep, voluptuous voice of Emeli Sandé in her majestic song "*Clown*". A moment later, my favorite smoothie in hand, I sank into a thick, comfortable couch, took a deep breath, and closed my eyes, savoring the moment. I had just avoided a big loss. Having escaped a bull trap in one of the indices, I had been able after a couple of restless days and nights to reverse my positions at the right levels and time, turning that loss into a profit, which deserved a little break; a moment of self-reflection.

As far as I can remember, this was the path I had chosen. For when at sixteen, my father asked me what I wanted to do right after school and heard my reply — aviation pilot — his immediate response had been: "*You will study to become a doctor or work as a garbage collector.*"

Two years later, after finishing school I cleaned out my savings account, packed my bag, and landed in Los Angeles, California with a couple thousand dollars in my pocket, odd jobs in the pipeline to pay for my physical education tuition, perfect my jab, face my fears and test my will in boxing rings. Chance later brought me back to real estate and then aviation when I had the time and money, and I wouldn't have done it any other way because nothing matches walking the unbeaten trails and drawing our own print in earth's dust and mud, which is where we are all coming from.

We spend half our life being taught what to think, do, and say, and if we're lucky, the other half trying to unlearn it in order to realize our true self and potential, and find our way back to what we were destined to be. I was lucky enough not to have wasted all that time from the beginning, and very glad to have chosen trial and error and sweat and blood over the comfort and safety of my home or some alluring wall diploma. Having survived the streets of Beirut, LA, and NY, and completed my formal education on gym floors and in boxing rings, I had developed a distinctive disposition, resilience and tolerance — most necessary, I discovered later, for the stock market. All this is history now, and fades to insignificance next to my late st trials and tribulations, for which I owe my survival to an endless insatiable thirst for learning as well as a little shiny star in the dark skies.

A young couple were holding hands, kissing each other with tender love and care. The boy was showing his girl a lot of respect and attention, not like some macho guys who feel compelled to act arrogant and superior according to certain social and cultural molds and masks, or because of deep ingrained fears and insecurities brought about by the beauty and freedom of an educated, independent woman. This macho attitude happens to be, and contrary to what they might think or believe, a latent form of homosexuality.

Man's best pastime has always been war, while woman's has been love and life-giving. History is supposed to be a springboard to the future, not some self-glorifying, self-gratifying, boasting, ruminating station and proxy for wars, aggressions and cults of personalities. However more often than not, it ends up being misunderstood, misinterpreted and misused. No violence — physical or otherwise — has ever brought justice or a solution to a problem, yet stories of myths, glories and illusory victories still abound in history books and create in the individual a sense of self-importance, chauvinism, and bigotry.

I had discovered a few years back that we are our own worst enemy; that life is an individual battle between one and oneself and not an organized collective endeavor against others; that we build egos and social masks as scarecrows to deter; that we are scared and insecure on the inside, no matter how we appear on the outside; that most of the blows we receive are merely bruises to our egos, but also life's gift for progress in our perpetual journey; that a lot of superstitions around stem from our own projections onto others; that some people cultivate ugliness over beauty in a defensive, preventive way; that the pen is mightier than the sword, and whoever kills in the name of God is the enemy of life and of its designer, because life is a gift and a cycle, and they would be guilty of interrupting it. Most importantly I discovered that fundamental cultural differences lie between the sterile search for morals and meanings on the existential level and the search for universal values and ethics on the pragmatic one, which leads inevitably to assuming responsibility based on the Golden Rule of consensual reciprocity, equal gender rights, freedom of thought and expression, respect for others or any other creature that crawls the earth, because every organism, movable or immovable, has a purpose.

My train of thought was floating over all these places when my couch quivered like someone had just bumped into it. As I opened my eyes, emerging from my meditation, a guy in his mid-fifties, Kangol cap over his head, a steaming beverage in hand, was passing me by. I could see from his back he had a tall emancipated shape and a gait that felt familiar. He also displayed a ponytail and an unshaven gray beard, but it wasn't until he turned as if to excuse himself that I was able to recognize who he really was.

"Hey! It is good to see you here again, Mister," he said with that nagging smile. "Where is your trading hardware?"

"Pythagoras! Good to see you here too. It's a well-deserved day off today. How have you been?" I returned his smile, knowing from my previous encounter this would not be a fortuitous meeting and nothing is left to chance with this guy.

"Well, you know what they say: '*Satisfaction is the mother of content*'. Do you mind if I share that place with you?"

I was pleased to see him again, and as he pulled up a chair and settled down across from me, I said, "You know, it's been hard the past couple of weeks. I lost and recovered a substantial sum of money, but ended up with a nice little profit, so I went out to blow off some steam."

"Tell me about it. Would you mind?" He settled his cup on the table as I looked at him with amazement and respect. A lot of strength and wisdom were emanating from this man, not in terms of brute physical force, but from within: from a sense of knowledge and understanding.

"It was a bull trap. I fell victim to my own greed, over-confidence and a sequence of flawless trades."

"Hmm, trading is a very rewarding yet unforgiving discipline. If you overtrade, you burn yourself, and if you don't, you lose the touch. You have to balance between the markets and your personal life."

Two young women with Fibonacci proportions passed us by. Most probably looking for a place to settle down and unload their secrets, one could tell from their apparent verve and complicity. We looked at them together in appreciation.

"Balance is a very elusive word, Pythagoras. It is more like tightrope walking nowadays."

"Balance is very important, Mario. Everything in life is Karma, fractals and proportionality. As for the effects, the causes go back in time, and our genes as far as our ancestors and creation. Everything in this universe is a manifestation and distribution of the fifth element, the element of love, according to a cosmic balance sheet. And don't forget, trading is Technical Analysis, risk management, and psychology, the latter being the most critical."

Oops, I thought. I felt it was coming. *Let's see what he's got in his bag this time...*

"You have to know yourself, dude. Do you use checklists?"

"I do, but sometimes I feel compelled to act out of boredom or excitement."

"Yes... overtrading is one of the most recurring mistakes in the markets. Patience is a virtue, delayed over immediate gratification and, most importantly, selectivity according to the highest criteria. This is why one of the most vital tasks in everything you do is to know your true motives.

"Why do you trade? Most of the time, we do anything in the absence of better choices and end up messing up. This world is spinning and all this activity is the search for love: attention by acknowledgment and validation. Everybody wants to be right. The market depicts all this activity, and that is the captivating thing about it, especially when it is translated into something concrete: money, which is nothing other than a conventional reward, a substitute to gauge and measure human labor and activity. In a psychosomatic world operating on myths and beliefs, the smallest currencies are ideas in our daily interactions that require attention of our five senses on the parasympathetic system. Once our senses are moderated they awaken the sixth, which is subjective intuition at first then objective premonition. Something that can occur only after the feminine/masculine sides and the impulses of life and death are balanced.

"You've got to clear your mind before you trade. It is, as you said, like tightrope walking: a fine line between antagonists, mainly our animus and anima, subjectivity versus objectivity, lust and hate, selfishness versus selflessness. Trading with high expectations can be very dangerous. In this current macho world run by men, woman is the most sought after and desired of God's creations, which is why any culture that does not respect this universal principle is doomed to remain unbalanced, dysfunctional, and aggressive, even though it might pretend otherwise or lay the blame on others or some conspiracy theory. You can measure the level of peacefulness, or conversely aggressiveness, in a culture by the presence of liberated women in the streets and the proximity of birds to people in public places. Demography is a culprit, mixed with spiritual greed on the existential level called religion. Everybody wants to be like God and achieve immortality, and it all falls into spiritual and biogenetical greed, emotional immaturity and parental authority replacement.

"'*God is a comedian playing to an audience that is too afraid to laugh*' cared to remind us Voltaire, one of the brightest minds of the 17th century. People live in the mode of 'having' instead of the mode of 'being' nowadays: having a big house, a big car, a big bank account, a docile wife, a big religious faith and an additional eternal life. Religion is not only the opiate of the masses, but of the fear of death, and the more this fear is denied and repressed, the more aggressiveness and violence it begets by implosion or explosion. All these dos and don'ts generate a lot of people's frustrations, repressions, and neuroses. Instead of accepting and assuming responsibility for life's natural cycle and understanding of death, they choose to live in fantasies and renunciation. No society is balanced without the free feminine element, yet man invented a long time ago the Apple Myth to manipulate and control the woman by burdening her with a guilt complex."

As he paused to catch his breath, James Brown's most notorious song *"It's a Man's Man's Man's World"* was now playing on the airwaves in an unequivocal act of synchronicity.

"You know, Mario, women are better traders than us. If you teach a woman to trade, she will set her mind to make enough money for her next Louis Vuitton or Chanel acquisition." He laughed kind-heartedly. "They have a stronger psychology than us. Just like the time and price axis on the chart and the divine geometry for which the 45-degree angle is the center of gravity, people will swing and vibrate around your time and space in life depending on their levels of love or hate, refinement or coarseness, and needs for attention and acknowledgment. Likewise, the 45-degree angle in the stock market reveals all this activity and volatility around it and the chaos happening in the world today because of disparities in cultures and ever-growing demography. The internet and user-friendly platforms introduced new participants from various cultural backgrounds and time and money expectations, and thus changed the paradigms of the market, not to mention algorithmic robotic 'High Frequency Trading'. Just like climate change, volatility is here to stay, and its main causes are man-made: discrepancies in cultures; spiritual and biogenetical greed; and demographics, the latter being by far the most lethal to the planet and its ecology.

"In the 18th century, Thomas Robert Malthus warned us of its consequences only to be accused of being inhuman and insensitive. It has gotten worse in our times. If one person can generate a number of problems and inflict a degree of damage to the environment and the planet, two, three, and five individuals will multiply these problems and damages exponentially, and that level is neither manageable nor reversible in the short term. But politicians and people in decision-making places suffer from an Ostrich Syndrome by not addressing those problems in a frontal manner but rather applying to them Band-Aids and a Botox therapy. The internet and global communications opened a Pandora's Box for which the world was not prepared.

"Take the time to relax, man, to replenish your resources and balance your physical and mental states before you trade. Your center of gravity lay between your feminine and masculine provinces."

As I swallowed my pride and hid my shame, knowing I was guilty of most of what he was inferring, I uttered, "But how do we overcome, transcend this entire complicated situation?"

"We come to this life with a predisposition that is commonly called determinism and a free will, but it is actually a book half-written and a pen life endows us with. You have the ability to complete, rewrite the story, and here lies the difference between fate and destiny. You are a free person with your own choices and responsibilities, assume this responsibility.

"May I ask you what system you use for trading?"

"For sure," I replied. "Mostly the Dow Theory, Elliott Wave and Ichimoku for evaluation, but Gann Method for execution."

"The Dow Theory and Ichimoku are clear objective systems; however Elliott Wave is nice only in theory. In an exemplary world it depicts a unique human behavior that occurs sometimes in practice, sometimes not. Unfortunately, no two Elliotticians agree on the waves' structure so it is most of the time like a Rorschach test: not very clear, abstract and very subjective. The error most technicians do is to force the count on every market and every timeframe. Yes, there are long and short waves in the market, but their occurrence and configuration are at times arbitrary and do not emulate the perfect portrayed model. The anatomy and rhythm of the markets have changed with the inflow of capitals from different cultures that have various behavior models and therefore reactions to events; not to mention machines psychology trading. In a fast moving and unpredictable market you need a simpler system and to constantly monitor and reassess yourself and expectations. There are three phases in the markets: accumulation; participation; and distribution. You know where you want to be."

"You know, that's easier said than done. After a while we get addicted to the market. We miss the adrenaline when we don't trade."

"I know what you mean. People criticize the likes of Soros, Buffett, and Gates because of their considerable accumulated wealth, but remember all these shrewd investors bought when everybody was fearful and sold when everybody was confident. And they forget that these people, although not always for the best philanthropic incentives, have contributed to more good than all the synagogues, churches, and mosques combined, with no stains of blood on their hands. I am not saying that we should be condoning neither the ruthlessness of capitalism nor the oppressiveness of communism, but what I am rather implying is that we should start seriously thinking about a new system and a new way to manage our affairs on this very precious planet. Some sort of social democracy or democratic socialism based not on Karl Marx's or Adam Smith's conflicting ideologies, but on mending the gaps between them: wage disparities, gender equity and human rights, while providing basic needs and integrity to every human being according to the

United Nations Charter within the respect of our planet and its ecology."

"But all this is massive, Pythagoras — Titanic!"

"The alternative, my friend, *is* Titanic. People bicker over details and take part in senseless debates about who is right and who is wrong and confuse the form for the content of the messages. Take creation and evolution, for example. They feel compelled to take a stand regarding this or that, but where is the big deal if there was one or the other or both at the same time, some sort of creative evolution or evolutionary creation? Do they really think the creator needs their help and assistance on this one? Or would they rather care that they need to find the right path to be just, virtuous, and peaceful in this world by their own means and merits? Everybody is confusing the form for the content of the messages like an egg and chicken riddle and getting drawn into a puddle of water. The purpose of life is to realize your humanity by balancing yourself between opposites on the 45-degree angle."

As the night had shifted and thrown its cloak outside on the fading remaining daylight, gold was now finishing a fifty percent correction while crossing back the 200 MA, respecting a major long-term trend line.

* * *

When I first came across a financial chart, it felt as if it was trying to tell me something I did not understand. Nevertheless, with my obstinate, recalcitrant mind

I got into the investment I wasn't supposed to enter. It was then that a search for a method that would allow me dealing with the markets began. My enduring quest ended what I am today: a technical analyst. I had to learn it like everything else in my life: the hard way.

Soon after, I was about to discover along the financial world, the most vibrant, dynamic and passionate of all disciplines, as necessity is the mother of invention.

Everything in nature obeys and responds to certain laws and rules; call them natural, cosmic, civil or divine. Financial markets are no exception. Some mystics found it exotic to brand them esoteric, while other existentialists call them religious. Some very wise men entrusted them the label alchemy, and later on, science.

Ever since the dawn of time, humans have observed regularities in life and nature. It was the Greek philosopher/mathematician Pythagoras who, about 500 BC, coined the word *Phi*, short of 1.618, the '*Golden Number*'. It was developed centuries later by another mathematician, Leonardo de Pisa, aka Fibonacci (AD 1170–1250), in the sequence of numbers most famous for carrying his name, 'the Fibonacci sequence'. Later, around AD 1452–1519, came an artist/scientist by the name of Leonardo da Vinci and used these same ratios and proportions generating masterpieces in painting and art. It wasn't until the late 1930s that Ralph Nelson Elliott from Marysville, KS (1871-1948) introduced these numbers and proportions to financial markets while seeking to improve on the Dow Theory, coming up with his own Elliot Wave Theory.

While in physics, physicists argue the case of cause and effect, the most famous being Newton's Third Law of Motion, reality might actually be a bit different, or shall we say Newton's statement not so accurate or up-to-date in today's world of knowledge. As if in practice there was an opposite and equal reaction to every action, the world would be flat in 'technical terms' with everything in a linear or sideways movement, which is not exactly the case. As actually everything moves in circles, or rather in spirals following specific proportions. This is where the Golden Number Phi comes to mind.

If we were to take demography and inflation, for example, and plot them on a chart, we could discover they move hand in hand and follow a certain growth pattern. Aging, maturing, our emotional states, and the Yin and Yang, the feminine and masculine aspects of every part of creation, follow that same rhythm as well. From the shells of the snail, oyster and nautilus up to the largest celestial objects that gravitate above our heads in the nightly sky there are analogies, fractals and proportionality, all measured and fathomed by 1.618: 'The Universal Secret Code'.

Behind the apparent chaos of life lurks God's signature: law and order — universal order. This was one of the beautiful truths I discovered with Technical Analysis.

13. Market Timing

As my passion and interest for Technical Analysis grew so did my knowledge. I had come across some dynamic principles, applicable to the economy and life; some people could have easily exploited and called them 'truths'. Yet, honest philosophers and scientists call them as they are: principles and science.

More than ever and since the inception of the Internet, the telecom revolution, computers, software and technical tools, the need for a market strategy has become more important. In a world moving and interacting at the speed of light: the speed of airwaves and internet data flows and connections, the implementation of a Market Timing strategy could separate the winners from the losers, the survivors from the 'wannabes' and 'would-have-been'.

In order to talk about Market Timing, we have to distinguish some nuances in the financial vocabulary. Market Timing is a strategy, relying on facts with a precise set of rules that allows us to buy and sell, enter and exit the market based on certain criteria and references. It is not Market Cycle Theory, which is a market forecast method attempting to predict where the price will be in the future based on amplitudes, periods, phases and left/right translations.

The market has three tendencies: uptrend; downtrend; and sideways ranges. There will always be periods of boom and bust (bulls and bears) in the market. If we look at any time frame chart, we notice price moves a third of the time up, a third of the time sideways in periods of indecision, rest or consolidation and a third of the time down; thus, the relevance to implement a strategy to be well-positioned on the right side of it and benefit from all situations. Before the introduction and development of Technical Analysis, a buy and hold strategy using Fundamental Analysis was the safest way not to lose money for the long term investor, since any unrealized loss or gain in the market was irrelevant as long as we hadn't exited our positions and concretized it. We could have held on to it indefinitely until the end of a recession or bear market if we didn't need the invested money.

Nevertheless, if we had bought stocks in 1929, it would have taken twenty-five years to break even, and from 1966 to 1983, seventeen years. From January 2000 up until February 2013, the DJI had been fluctuating between the 11,500 and 14,000 levels, so does a buy and hold strategy still sound convincing? How many times would a good Market Timing strategy have returned throughout these last thirteen years? Buy and hold is passive, while Market Timing is an active involvement in the stock market. Applied with a high degree of discipline, diligence and a well-thought plan, it helps benefit from these long-term conditions and be on the right side of the equation.

Studies and statistics done by 'very bright people' have demonstrated the following effects on financial markets: 'the Halloween Effect' or 'sell in May and go away'. September is, in general, the worst and January the best month of the year. Moon cycles, sunspots and many other situations affect our financial world. If the moon and stars can have an effect on the ebb and flow of the seas, you can almost be sure they would also affect our mood, behavior and consequently the stock market. Major elections, such as presidential in some countries, can have a direct or indirect impact on the global economy as well, especially if the country in question is the size of the United States in terms of foreign policy, production, consumption, innovation, research and development.

As such, the U.S. presidential election and the political party favored in that election play a key role in the U.S. economy, maybe because of the need for change or the new hopes they bring with it. In general, the following presidential cycle has been noticed in the United States stock market: the first and fourth years following the presidential elections are positive; the second and third years post-election are negative. However, this is just an observation and can never be relied upon as a rule.

There are also people who like to buy or sell when there is a percentage change in an index or indicator; a three to four percentage mark is usually taken into consideration.

In today's fast moving world, studying the markets using Fundamental Analysis, economic reports and information like 'buy on rumor/sell on the news', employment, Consumer Price Reports, Producer Price Index, Beige Book, Housing Starts, Leading Economic Indicator, Gross Domestic Products, interest rates, P/E, EPS, Alpha, Beta, Omega, etc. can be very risky and requires a lot of time, research, experience, as well an austere risk and money management plan. It is not about these reports but how the market will react and respond to them. They might be, as in most times, mere catalysts for an already ripe market condition.

We can try timing the market using these fundamental reports, presidential cycles, seasonal cycles, January effect, Santa Claus, the Valentine effect or the flip of a coin, but whichever system we choose, patience, discipline and consistency must be the order of the day. Technical Analysis, if well applied, gives us the best and most accurate timing tool because it constantly measures the strengths and weaknesses of the market from a yearly basis and perspective, down to the minute.

In order to time the market, some basic knowledge of Technical Analysis such as the geometrical use of trend lines and arithmetic use of moving averages and oscillators on the chart is required. And after all, a picture is worth a thousand words.

In conclusion, Market Timing is a strategy not a forecast system. It is a discipline that helps us, if well applied, be on the right side of the market. Whatever our trading style: methodology, consistency and a mechanical way of thinking and execution are important to remove the interference of subjectivity and emotions from the activity at hand. Bearing in mind that financial markets are the reflection of human behavior and crowd psychology; after all we are emotional beings who respond collectively to emotional stimulus and our surrounding. Set reasonable goals; little by little, the bird builds its nest.

14. The Ichimoku Kinkō Hyō

From the first time one gets interested in the world of trading and investing the quest for a holy grail begins; the search for a system that provides an instantaneous and objective evaluation of the market condition. One of the best comprehensive and independent systems I came across was the Ichimoku Kinkō Hyō, aka IKH, and more so since Pythagoras alluded to it. But before delving into its substance, we ought to put it in the adequate historical context to disclose the wisdom, astuteness, and farsightedness of its design.

Like the seismologist or cardiologist, the technical analyst studies the charts, trying to detect subtle moves that have predictive values. Some cycle analysts have gone as far as comparing various waves and cycles in nature and the financial world to the beats of the heart: J. M. Hurst's *Profit Magic of Stock Transaction Timing* (1970) and Tony Plummer's *Law of Vibration* (2013). From the three types of Technical Analysis: classical; mathematical; and cyclical; it would be realistic to consign the last two to the IKH: calculated with mathematical formulas based on cycle theories.

Although the recorded history of Technical Analysis seems recent, history points out that people like Pythagoras, Leonardo de Pisa and Leonardo da Vinci having discovered numbers, sequences and proportions in nature, used them in math, sciences, arts and other disciplines. In 1585 public quotes of over three hundred items were traded in the coffee shops of Amsterdam, and in 1608 one of the greatest and earliest exchanges, the 'Beurs', or Amsterdam Stock Exchange, was born. It became famous later, between 1636 and 1637, for the 'Tulip Bulb Mania', when the price of a single tulip bulb reached ten times the annual income of a skilled craftsman, then suddenly collapsed. It is considered to be the first speculative financial bubble, and is referred to by British journalist Charles Mackay in his book *Extraordinary Popular Delusions and the Madness of Crowds*, in 1841.

In the 18th century, a Japanese rice commodity trader by the name of Munehisa Homma (1724–1803) started recording the price of rice according to what we know today as Candlesticks, while at the same time in the West prices were being recorded under the Point and Figure chart format.

It wasn't until 1884, when Charles Dow introduced the Dow Theory and founded the first ever Stock Market Index, that 'modern' Technical Analysis was born.

The Dow Theory premises:

- The averages discount everything
- The market has three trends or tendencies: up; down; and sideways
- Major trends have three phases: accumulation; participation; and distribution
- The averages must confirm each other
- Volume must confirm the trend
- A trend is intact until it gives a definite reversal signal

In 1939, a Japanese journalist by the name of Goichi Hosoda ran tests and calculations with the help of a group of his assistants, for over a period of more than twenty years, to come up in 1968 with a trading system he called the Ichimoku Kinkō Hyō, meaning 'equilibrium chart at a glance'. The application offered multiple tests, mainly through three indicators, thus offering three diverse signals on the same chart. However, it delivered much more to the eye of the seasoned analyst.

Moving Averages have been used in artillery, rocket science, and statistics since the beginning of the 19th century, but their application to the stock market came later, between 1930 and 1960, when various types of Moving Averages were calculated and used to measure strengths and weaknesses in prices. From Simple to Exponential, Triangular, Weighted, Adaptive or Displaced, Moving Averages were calculated and applied directly on the chart.

But the Displaced characteristics were the most important aspect of the IKH as they were used for cycle isolation and the role reversal qualities of support and resistance.

The Moving Average crossovers and the '4-Weeks Rule', promoted by Richard Donchian across the Pacific approximately at the same time of Mr. Hosoda's findings, were some of the same basic principles of the IKH. Similarities also occurred between the IKH 'Kumo' cloud and Gerald Appel's 1970s MACD (Moving Average Convergence-Divergence) indicator, and are yet more signs of Mr. Hosoda's ingenuity.

Since the IKH was initially built and tested on daily charts, it shows us the price today in relation to a 26-day period in the past, equivalent to 4 weeks with the shifting backward of the Chikou Span (the closing price line), as well as a 26-day period into the future, again equivalent to 4 weeks with the shifting forward of the Kumo cloud. Therefore 26 days are equivalent to the 4-Weeks Rule Mr. Donchian promoted in his Commodities and Futures Trading System at the same time across the Pacific. What these 26-day periods are effectively telling us on the daily chart is that the price today is higher, lower, or equal to the price 26 days ago and 26 days later.

Additionally, the Tenkan-Sen and Kijun-Sen offer support and resistance for the actual price while the Kumo cloud defines the trend drawing future support or resistance. The thickness or thinness of the cloud measures as well, just like Bollinger Bands, the volatility of the market, and forecasts the strength or weakness of this future support or resistance, while the cloud's Senkou Spans A and B crossover and the price perform like an MACD, interacting directly with the price with all the MACD features. This will be clarified in the ensuing explanation.

All the Moving Averages calculations of the IKH are based on the 50% retracement of their respective periods (highest high + lowest low/2). Therefore, the 9 period Tenkan-Sen and the 26 period Kijun-Sen are akin to weekly and monthly 50% retracements applied on the daily chart, providing more reliable support and resistance than normally calculated Moving Averages. The Senkou Span B, with its 26 period projection forward, is also laying ahead a monthly 50% retracement for the future, at the same time acting like an interactive MACD Middle Line for the price on the chart, while the Senkou Span A, which is an average of the Tenkan-Sen and Kijun-Sen, acts as an MACD Line. The periods of the Senkou Span A and MACD Line are very close and similar in principle, as they are both an average of two Moving Averages. One is calculated by addition then division by two, the other by subtraction between the two. Their ensuing results are pretty close (Senkou Span A = Tenkan-Sen + Kijun-Sen/2 = 17.5, while in the MACD case: 26 EMA − 12 EMA = 14). Moreover, the cloud width acts like an MACD Histogram and is indicative of present volatility, while the twists of Spans A and B are similar to a crossing of the Histogram above or below the Middle Line.

The overall advantages of the IKH in general, and of its Kumo cloud in particular, are all the aforementioned features plus their direct application over the price, making the IKH a highly dynamic and interactive visual sort of MACD along with all the relative signals of Gerald Appel's application, the Moving Averages method, 50% retracements for different periods, and Richard Donchian's 4-Weeks rule, plus two additional features: trend definition; and future support and resistance delineation.

Until you gain a better understanding of the founding principles of the system, the IKH lends itself quite well for use at all levels. In its most basic interpretation, one first starts defining the trend in one's chosen timeframe: uptrend; downtrend; or sideways respectively if the price is above, below, or within the cloud. Subsequently, any confirmed signal from the upward crossover of the Tenkan-Sen over the Kijun-Sen while the price is above the cloud and the Chikou Span above the price is a good buy signal, while it is deemed a weak signal if the price is below the cloud. Any short signal, such as downward crossover of the Tenkan-Sen over the Kijun-Sen while the price is below the cloud and the Chikou Span is below the price is a good sell signal, and considered a weak signal if the price is above the cloud. Finally, any long or short signal when the price is within the cloud boundaries is deemed neutral.

Like many aspects of the Japanese culture, the IKH bears a lot of wisdom and strength in its conception, and after so many years one can only stand in admiration of one Japanese man's vision and foresight. But while the IKH is an awesome and complete trading system, we can never remind ourselves enough of the market's hazards and vagaries, and that in order to be a successful trader, two main qualities are necessary: humility; and an immeasurable thirst for learning.

15. The Final Call

The engine was screeching as I passed the speeding cars, flowing in random yet orderly akin patterns. As I shifted to a higher gear, releasing the pistons from their accumulated pressure, forging my way along the airport road, my mind began perceiving the traffic's rhythm, gaps and distances calculating their Moving Average.

"The chart is your treasure map; follow the chart"; the sentence kept flashing in my thoughts as I piloted the motorbike. Ever since a financial chart had popped up on my screen, I'd felt it was telling me something I did not understand. It took me many years to learn to decipher and interpret its messages.

In science, the time parameter is often inclusive in the formula. Reality, it has been said, is a theater: a context within which we interact to conduct our daily chores and businesses, but is also dependent on a confluence of factors, most importantly the geographical location and period of our times. Life is smoke and mirrors. Things are most of the time not what they appear to be as we are living on the edge of two worlds. The first of ethereal nature, the second of matter: a psychosomatic world of ideas and beliefs where every physical manifestation is a tip of an iceberg, merely a symbol and representation of what lies ahead or beneath. And in order to see beyond this veil of illusion, one owes to moderate the senses, cleaning them from all relative convictions, associations, projections and expectations, tuning in an objective form of perception.

The Bluetooth was now playing Isabelle Boulay's song "*Mille après Mille*" in my helmet as I negotiated the last turn before the airport's parking entrance. The French have always been the champions of many things, among them laying the principles of humanism and later on, after the Greeks, refining democracy, and I have a great deal of respect for their Enlightenment era philosophers. But people from the Middle East only picked and embraced their most useless pastime: nostalgic romanticism and melancholia — emotional elation for ego exaltation.

The West has since made two quantum leaps that have separated it from the rest of the world. It moved from the age of religion and emotions to the age of reason and thoughts in the 18th century, and then to science, psychology and introspection, drawing a road map to the boundless human brain and drafting a Social Contract in which it consolidated freedoms of thought, expression and woman's equality. There are stages of narcissism directly related to psychosexual developments and balance of genders in the individual that might correspond to these same periods of change for a culture and society. Any excessive authority, such as dictatorships or theocracies, will only breed deprivation, frustration and emotional dependency, resulting sooner or later in conformism and followers of cults of the personalities.

The air felt damp and chilly in the underground parking level and I loved the smell and feel of it, as this was always a preliminary moment to an inevitable forthcoming contextual shift. Airport hubs and gates are doors of perception, for every destination transports us to a different environment: a different reality woven and produced by its people's ideas, system of beliefs and mythology.

Having found a secure place for my motorbike, I left it resting on the side stand and made my way to the tunnel leading to the terminal building. The lady issuing the boarding passes was smiling. The immigration officer was of a totally different league and attitude: serious and stern, dictated by his job and responsibility.

The bar was still empty in the early hours except for two couples: one British; the other of Middle-Eastern ethnicity, the woman distinguishing herself in a veil. The British foresaw the importance of the matriarchal rule, and here resides the success of their nation's history. The veil is a big issue in Europe, and elsewhere, nowadays, and although its rhetorical meanings, justifications and explanations are diverse and used at best in the political and religious discourse and arena, it has the potential to bring Europe back to the brink of the first developmental phase by reinstituting the Religious Contract and unbalancing the roles of woman and man in society.

"One Carlsberg, please," I asked the bartender while unstrapping my backpack and putting it on the floor, as I always enjoyed the exquisite savor of a good beer anytime of the day before a new journey.

"Beer is on me this time", a voice sprang from behind my left shoulder.

As I spun to see where it was coming from, I came face to face with a familiar look.

"Do we always have to meet like this, Pythagoras?" I joked, my face breaking into a smile.

"My friend, you've been in my thoughts lately. How have you been? Where are you taking off to today?"

"I am following my bliss. Flying to London, and where are you heading?"

"To Greece ... the country's calling. We still have a few hours, I believe. Would you like to pass them together?"

He paid and we made our way to a nearby table. "Tell me first, how's your trading?" he asked as we sat down.

"My technical skills have made significant progress since we last met. I have researched and introduced new methodologies, but still have to work on my psychology," I laughed.

"Very good... Acknowledging one's weakness is a virtue, indeed. You know, any experiment under the ideal laboratory conditions of temperature, humidity and atmospheric pressure produces consistent results. In real life, however, where these parameters vary, the outcome is always different. Trading and Technical Analysis are no exceptions. Trading and investing are subject to statistics and probabilities: once you've found your entry and exit points and devised a plan, the most difficult part is to put your ego to sleep and follow that plan meticulously. The market is the variable; you have to be that consistency. Studying and analyzing charts is one thing, trading is a totally different undertaking. As soon as you push the buy or sell button and commit to a trade, a series of chemical reactions kicks off in your body and your mood becomes connected to your new position. This is the most difficult part of trading. This is where knowledge, experience and psychology combined come into play."

"Wow, I never realized it is so complex. I mean, chemically speaking," I uttered. This guy had the capacity to always keep me flabbergasted, on the edge of my curiosity.

"All this advertising about easy money, low financial costs and speed of execution is a big fiddle," he continued "To entice people to enter the market, overtrade and fall into the sins and traps of trading. Trading is not a game, nor for the faint-hearted; it is a very serious business. There are two opposite forces in that market, and if you don't study them well they can harm you. There are a thousand ways to tackle Mr. Market, but the most important are managing risk and an unfettered psychology. The market is a five-day hard work round, two-day rest — you know how many rounds amateurs go and pros last. Most people on the short term charts are sitting ducks for the big guys with the big guns to slaughter."

I couldn't refrain from laughing. I am sometimes a sitting duck myself, but I'd like to meet that guy with the gun to show him my colors and the number of rounds we could go, I thought to myself.

"If I gave you a thousand dollars today and asked you to buy me an ounce of gold," he went on "How many do you think you would be able to acquire? Barely one. These video-game-style platforms are giving you one in a hundred leverage and above, so that if the price moves one percent or less, you could say I held a hundred ounces of gold for two minutes before I lost them. And they do this on the short term charts, with the next expiration date over-the-counter contracts, to make you historically blind-sighted, keep you under pressure and rolling over. People get in trouble for getting caught up in this challenge."

This guy was either a master of ceremonies or the most providential guy on earth, for as he paused to drink from his beer, the airport sound system was playing Kenny Rogers's song *"The Gambler"*. My eyes and ears were wide open, and my jaw dropped as I moved closer to the table. Pythagoras was in the bull's-eye, and I felt also guilty of what he was referring to.

"Have you ever heard of the pillow test, Mario?"

"Not that I know of, no! Is it something related to pregnancy?" I inquired surprised.

He almost fell off his chair as he exploded laughing, held himself up, looked me in the eyes then said,

"Yes my friend, something similar, but related to your financial endeavor. If you are unable to sleep at night without waking-up every few hours to check on your positions then something is not right. Let me put it for you in a different way. If your investment is too exciting and thrilling, it is wrong. A sound investment is supposed to be boring."

"Very interesting! So no adrenaline from investing," I replied jokingly.

"When you spend enough time in the markets studying charts, you start blending Candles in your mind and perceiving Moving Averages. But do not underestimate the psychosomatic qualities of life. Everyone wants to be right, and you will not succeed until you understand why you trade and get to know your true motives.

"I will tell you a secret, Mario. I'm a technical analyst as well, and when I look at a historical demography chart, it scares me. We might be in the mother of all bubbles in human history. This whole economy is dependent on a vicious and unsustainable cycle of production, consumption and a barrel of oil, relying on a never-ending growing demography at the expense of the planet's ecology. Inflation is a consequence of demography: we print money to provide for the newborn, therefore depreciate the purchase power of currency. Gold is a benchmark for inflation and therefore is money; because it is the only commodity quoted in all currencies.

"Some people like stocks, others like sugar, coffee, corn or cotton, and both are right as there are times for everything. But if someone was watching us from Mars and believed we were crazy acquiring gold, they would also think the same about IBM, Coca Cola, General Motors and General Electric. If you calculate the compounded growth of population and compare it to that of inflation, you will notice they go hand in hand and follow nearly the same pattern over the decades. Devise a plan and respect it religiously."

"I thought you didn't appreciate religion, Pythagoras. How come you associate it to trading?" I teased.

"People name 'religion' whichever system of thoughts that has caused wars and plight then offered them protection from the fears of aging and death. But God is their ultimate archetype, pretention and ambition. They follow the archetype, not the real message. There are two folds in religions: existential; and ethical. They are only interested in the first to save their souls and secure for themselves a seat in heaven. But if Mickey Mouse came today and caused so much dread, dead and texts written in blood, they would follow him, honor him and recite blindly his story.

"I've seen more good people outside religion than inside of it, and they have far more merits because they are not acting such out of fear of some parental figure or in search of some glory. You think your conflict in the Middle East is about a piece of real estate and an olive tree? Think again. Read well the *Bible*. It's all about a four-thousand-year-old myth symbolizing the rivalry for a father, and the role of the mother in a patriarchal or otherwise matriarchal family model and society.

"The real God is out there and can be found neither in a synagogue, church or mosque, but everywhere and all around us in nature if we open our eyes and senses. It is only through the painting that one can appreciate and communicate with its artist."

As the PA system was announcing the boarding of our mutual flights, I shook Pythagoras's hand and bid him farewell. He then took a scroll from his bag and handed it to me. While he was doing so, he got closer and whispered to my ear, "Gaia sends you her regards." I didn't have the time to think or say anything before he disappeared amid the growing crowd. Overwhelmed, it took me a while before I turned toward my gate and started walking. The welcoming aircrew was genuinely and inconspicuously courteous, which must have been related to the nature of this job and culture of the company. I checked the flickering screen of my phone before switching it off. Gold had been flirting with the 200 MA for a while now, and only time would tell when its real value would unfold and inflation will catch up with demography. When the Senkou Span A passes above or below the Senkou Span B and the Chikou Span above or below the price, while the Tenkan-Sen and Kijun-Sen crossover at the same time, you have a perfect storm brewing.

The cabin hostess offered champagne as the pilot leveled the plane at cruising altitude. I unfolded the scroll and started reading, *The Golden Principles*...

The Golden Principles

Appreciate the gift of life even when you are non-mindful. You will start perceiving blessings you never could foresee.

How do you fear a God who is the giver of this glorious land in all its beauty, infinite realities and wisdom of change?

Concerning the tragedies that happen, bear them with fortitude. Never complain, but strive toward them knowing that fate sends them as opportunities to better oneself.

Existence does not come by force; we will disappear from the surface of this earth without prior notice. If dusk went reckless on us, would we survive another dawn?

Some say the stars in the skies are the souls of the people who died. The celestial bodies that orbit high above our heads on a dark night are of the same structure as the tiniest particle that twirls in us; we are a recurrent letter in the bigger book of life. The substance is always the same; when the shape varies, only the name changes.

Honor nature and respect all creatures that walk, crawl or creep on Mother Earth. The rivers, winds and trees are witnesses to our thoughts, intents and deeds. By respecting life you are grateful to God.

No science has the exclusive explanation of this world. Likewise, no religion has the exclusive representation of God. There is no religion superior to love: every dogma is alienation and sclerosis.

This world is a spinning merry-go-round wherein our minds are kaleidoscopes projecting and perceiving a transient holographic reality that varies with distance and time from our mythology, past and subconscious mind.

Mythology, beliefs and ideas constitute our Core Beliefs Operating System that generates this reality as a medium for the exchange of two things to which there is no third: love or hate in our hearts.

Every person's core ego is made-up of this intrinsic love/hate equation inherited down the genealogical Karmic DNA. Use it at face value, knowing all this human tragicomedy is a simulation for the stimulation of the neurovegetative system with the token of attention on the senses. We are beliefs/ideas carriers — reality generators: love or hate exchangers.

Myths, archetypes and personas contain feminine/ masculine proportions related to our impulses of life and death. Women bear love and bring a culture of life; men make war and harvest a culture of death. Our chances for success or failure in transcending our narcissism and realizing our humanity depend on balancing these two antagonists: woman plus man equals human.

The refinement of a culture, within the boundaries of distance and time, is most visible in three areas: gender equity; table manners; and respect of the tax code and public places. After our basic needs for food, water, warmth and shelter are met; it is all about how the element of love flows in this culture through body language and non-verbal communications.

The family model is a microcosm to socio-political realities in which the role of the father and the role of the mother fathom opportunities or encumbrances for emotional independency or remaining an adult child.

There are two types of people: existentialists consumed by the question of death and fearful father figure; and pragmatic epicureans motivated by the feminine creative side. The first aims at converting others by means of beards, attires, diets, prayers, and moralistic restrictions, ambitioning to get to the afterlife as soon as possible to meet their creator. The second endeavors to celebrate life in the best ethical ways of earthly accountability manifest in the cycles of birth and death, awakening and sleep, day and night, by cause/ effect, fractals, and proportionality.

Democracy is a matriarchal society, based on a Social Contract and driven by the impulse of life; it was founded on two inexorable principles: women's equality; and freedoms of thought and expression.

You cannot argue the second principle to override or reverse the first. Autocracies/kleptocracies and theocracies are patriarchal societies based on dictatorship or a Religious Contract; driven by the rule of men and the impulse of death; they are founded on cults of the identities, fear and intimidation. Two incompatible Core Beliefs Operating Systems: a Social versus a Religious Contract — a Matriarchal versus a Patriarchal society — a culture of life versus a culture of death.

Religion is an existential sickness exploiting the misunderstanding of death, and alienating the purpose of life: an ingratitude and inability of appreciating God's gift. The epitome of wisdom is the love of life.

All monotheistic religions are guilty of worshipping a 'man-god', therefore destined for war.

Man's ultimate drive for death comes from his misunderstanding of life and death alternating phases, and an unconscious desire to revisit the womb he comes from.

If you reconcile people with death you heal the world.

Open your eyes; you are in the Garden of Eden. An object does not exist without an observer; this world would not exist without us, as recipients and appreciators. We are the designer of our own gods and devils, hells and paradises. The real God is neither male nor female, nor black nor white, nor left nor right, and does not want to punish or reward us, but watches us from within, and sends us back to this life, as many times as necessary, to find the middle path and give birth to our humanity.

Life is a psychosomatic self-fulfilling prophecy.

We come to this life with a predisposition, what is commonly called determinism, and a free will, but it is actually a book half-written and a pen life endows us with. You have the ability to complete, rewrite the story; and here lies the difference between fate and destiny. You are a free person with your own choices and responsibilities, assume this responsibility.

There are many sorts of reasoning among men, good and bad. Do not be seduced or overwhelmed by their words or disguises. But arm yourself with patience, open-mindedness and critical thinking.

Never allow yourself to fall asleep at night until you have scrutinized your actions of the day. If you find in this self-appraisal that you have done wrong, better yourself, and if you have done right, stay humble and delight.

Knowing others is cleverness; knowing yourself is wisdom. Mastering others is strength; mastering yourself is true power. When you are strong, try lending a helping hand to the less strong, and when you are rich, try to care more for the less fortunate.

But remember: after the game is over, all the pieces go back into the same box.

Change your thoughts, and you will change your life. Live without judgments, definitions or convictions. The only conviction worth having is having none. Existence is movement and change. Rigidity leads to regression and decay.

Practice random acts of kindness. People live through each other by perceptual attention, but the excess of this need creates the narcissist.

Contemplate from a place at the periphery of the universe rather than its center, and whenever you are in doubt consult the Golden Rule of 'Consensual Reciprocity'.

A healthy mind in a healthy body is the adage of wise men.

Cultivate an ethical character and a sincere attitude. Refrain from violent behavior and practice diligence, respect and self-control. Pay attention to vanquishing Lust, Gluttony, Greed, Wrath, Envy, Sloth and Pride. Love, goodness and virtue spring from self-knowledge. Ignorance begets denial, evil and vice.

Breathing is a pleasure. We can live weeks without food, days without water and hours without heat, but only a few seconds without air. People forget that the moment 'past, future and present' is comprised in it. Live one breath at a time.

Whoever dwells on the past exists in expectations.

Accept uncertainty: don't get confused by the multiple facets of reality, it is impossible to comprehend, useless to explain. The purpose of life is every time and everywhere the same: balancing our feminine/masculine sides to overcome the narcissistic need for attention, and restore humanity through love in our heart.

If the only prayer you ever say in your whole life is "Thank you"; that would suffice.

In a system ruled by productivity, produce less and consume less. Leave your properties behind and travel around the world on a bike or a donkey to acquire wisdom, and regain your awe and appreciation.

The secret of happiness resides in the deliberateness of time.

Live your life in exclamation, not in explanation.

Notes

1   *Wear Sunscreen* is an essay written as a hypothetical commencement speech by columnist Mary Schmich, originally published in June 1997 in the Chicago Tribune. The essay became the basis for a successful spoken word song released in 1999 by Baz Luhrmann, *"Everybody's Free (To Wear Sunscreen)"*, also known as *"The Sunscreen Song"*, https://en.wikipedia.org/wiki/Wear_Sunscreen

2   *The Matrix*, directed by the Wachowski Brothers, Los Angeles: Warner Brothers and Village Roadshow Productions (1999).

3   This prayer is attributed to Travis Bowman and was found in Bess O'Connor, '*Clear Your Energy and Lift Your Spirits With the Sacred Art of Smudging*', Chopra.com, (n.d.), http://www.chopra.com/articles/clear-your-energy-and-lift-your-spirits-with-the-sacred-art-of-smudging#sm.00010lpecs1nfcyjqrf2f9811ltz6.

4   Discourse inspired by Native American Medicine Ways: Traditional Healers and Healing: The Medicine Wheel and the Four Directions. U.S. National Library of Medicine at: https://www.nlm.nih.gov/nativevoices/exhibition/healing-ways/medicine-ways/medicine-wheel.html

5   This saying has often been attributed to Cree Indians, although Quote Investigator.com has tentatively credited Alanis Obomsawin, an Abenaki from the Odanak reserve in Canada, who said this in a conversation with Ted Poole and was published as '*Conversations with North American Indians*', in Ralph Osborne (ed.) *Who is the Chairman of this Meeting?: A Collection of Essays*, Toronto: Neewin Publishing, p. 43.

6   Carl Abbott, '*Buddha's Four Noble Truths*', Center Tao, available at: http://www.centertao.org/essays/buddhas-four-noble-truths/, accessed 18 March 2017.

7   The Three Initiates, *The Kybalion: A Study of the Hermetic Philosophy of Ancient Egypt and Greece*. Chicago: Yogi Publication Society, (n.d.). Available at: http://www.hermetics.org/pdf/kybalion.pdf, p. 9.

8   George Long (transl.), *The Meditations of Marcus Aurelius*; reprinted many times, including in Vol. 2 of the Harvard Classics, (1862). Available at: https://en.wikipedia.org/wiki/Meditations.

9   Millennium Martial Arts & Fitness (Dojo Kun in English and Japanese) http://millenniummartialarts.com/dojo-kun/

10   Joseph Campbell, *The Power of Myth with Bill Moyers*, NY: Doubleday, (1988). https://en.wikiquote.org/wiki/Joseph_Campbell

11   Linda Adams, '*Learning a New Skill is Easier Said Than Done*', Gordon Training (2016). Available at: http://www.gordontraining.com/free-workplace-articles/learning-a-new-skill-is-easier-said-than-done/#.

12   http://biblehub.com/luke/6-29.htm

13   Albert Einstein *The World As I See It*, NYC: Philosophical Library (2010).

14   World Heritage Encyclopedia, *Jannah*, available at Free ebooks by Project Gutenberg, http://central.gutenberg.org/article/WHEBN0000507555/Jannah, accessed on 18 March 2017, and The Quran, Surat Al-Qital (The Fighting) 47:15.

15   Joseph J. Murphy, *Technical Analysis of the Financial Markets*, New York: New York Institute of Finance (1999) p. 2.

Bibliography

Armstrong, K. (1994). *A History of God*. New York: Ballantine Books.

Armstrong, K. (2014). *Fields of Blood: Religions and the History of Violence*. New York: Knopf.

Aurelius, M. (1997). *Meditations*. Mineola: Dover Publications.

Baudrillard, J. (1995). *Simulacra and Simulation*. Ann Arbor: University of Michigan.

Berne, E. (1996). *Games People Play: The Psychology of Human Relationships*. New York: Ballantine Books.

Boroden, C. (2008). *Fibonacci Trading: How to Master the Time and Price Advantage*. New York: McGraw-Hill Education.

Campbell, J. (1961). *A Skeleton Key to Finnegans Wake*. New York: Viking Press.

Campbell, J. (1972). *The Hero with a Thousand Faces*. Princeton: Princeton University Press.

Campbell, J. (1976). *The Masks of God: Complete Four Volume Set.* New York: Penguin Books.

Campbell, J. (1989). *Myths, Dreams and Religion.* Thompson: Spring Publications.

Campbell, J. (1991). *Creative Mythology.* New York: Penguin Books.

Campbell, J. (1991). *The Power of Myth.* New York: Anchor.

Campbell, J. (1999). *The Hero's Journey.* Rockport: Element Books Ltd.

Carroll, L. (1993). *Alice in Wonderland.* New York: Dover Publications, Inc.

Corrigan, J. (1997). *Jews, Christians, Muslims: A Comparative Introduction to Monotheistic Religions.* Upper Saddle River: Prentice Hall.

Elliott, N. (2007). *Ichimoku Charts: An Introduction to Ichimoku Clouds.* Hampshire: Harriman House.

Elliott, R.N. (2011). *Nature's Law: The Secret of the Universe.* Chicago: Snowball Publishing.

Elliott, R.N. (2012). *The Wave Principle.* Chicago: Snowball Publishing.

Frankl, V. (1988). *The Will to Meaning.* New York: Plume.

Frankl, V. (2000). *Man's Search for Meaning.* New York: Basic Books.

Freud, S. (1975). *Three Essays on the Theory of Sexuality.* New York: Basic Books.

Freud, S. (1990). *Beyond the Pleasure Principle.* New York: W. W. Norton & Co.

Freud, S. (1990). *The Ego and the Id*. New York: W. W. Norton & Co.

Freud, S. (1990). *Totem and Taboo*. New York: W. W. Norton & Co.

Freud, S. (1997). *Sexuality and the Psychology of Love*. New York: Touchstone.

Freud, S. (2001). *Moses and Monotheism*. New York: Vintage; New Ed.

Frost, A.J. & Prechter, R. (2001). *Elliott Wave Principle*. Hoboken: Wiley.

Fukuyama, F. (1992). *The End of History and the Last Man*. New York: Free Press.

Gann, W.D. (2008). *The Tunnel Thru the Air*. The Richest Man in Babylon Publisher.

Gann, W.D. (2008). *Truth of the Stock Tape*. The Richest Man in Babylon Publisher.

Gann, W.D. (2009). *45 years in Wall Street*. Eastford: Martino Fine Books.

Guthrie, W.K.C. (1977). *The Sophists*. Cambridge: Cambridge University Press.

Guthrie, W.K.C. (1979). A *History of Greek Philosophy Vol.1 & 2*. Cambridge: Cambridge University Press.

Hamilton, E. (2011). *Mythology: Timeless Tales of Gods and Heroes*. New York: Grand Central Publishing.

Hergenhahn, B.R. (1997). *An Introduction to the History of Psychology*. Pacific Grove: Brooks/ Cole Pub.

Hesse, H. (1981). *Siddhartha*. New York: Bantam.

Hurst, J.M. (1970). *The Profit Magic of Stock Transaction Timing.* Upper Saddle River: Prentice-Hall.

Huxley, A. (1932). *Brave New World.* London: Chatto & Windus.

Huxley, A. (1954). *The Doors of Perception.* New York: Harper & Bros.

James, W. (1983). *The Principles of Psychology, Vol.1 & 2.* Cambridge: Harvard University Press.

Jung, C.G. (1955). *Modern Man in Search of a Soul.* San Diego: Harcourt Brace.

Jung, C.G. (1968). *Man and his Symbols.* New York: Dell.

Jung, C.G. (1975). *Psychology and Religion: West and East.* Princeton: Princeton University Press.

Jung, C.G. (1976). *The Psychological Types.* Princeton: Princeton University Press.

Jung, C.G. (1980). *Psychology and Alchemy.* Princeton: Princeton University Press.

Jung, C.G. (1981). *The Archetypes and the Collective Unconscious.* Princeton: Princeton University Press.

Jung, C.G. (1998). *Synchronicity and the Paranormal.* Princeton: Princeton University Press.

Jung, C.G. (2003). *Psychology of the Unconscious.* Mineola: Dover Publications.

Kahn, C. (2011). *Pythagoras and the Pythagoreans.* Indianapolis: Hackett Publishing.

Kant, I. (1999). *Critique of Pure Reason.*
Cambridge: Cambridge University Press.

Keightley, T. (2010). *The Fairy Mythology.*
Charleston: Nabu Press.

Kennedy, R. (1983). *Hardcore Bodybuilding: The
Blood, Sweat and Tears of Pumping Iron.* New
York: Sterling Publishing.

Kuhn, T. (1996). *The Structure of Scientific
Revolutions.* Chicago: University of Chicago
Press.

Lake-Thom, B. (1997). *Spirits of the Earth.* New
York: Plume.

Lee, B. (1975). *Tao of Jeet Kune Do.* Los Angeles:
Ohara Publications.

Lévi-Strauss, C. (1974). *Structural Anthropology.*
New York: Basic Books.

Lévi-Strauss, C. (1988). *The Way of the Masks.*
Seattle: University of Washington.

Lévi-Strauss, C. (1995). *Myth and Meaning:
Cracking the Code of Culture.* New York:
Schocken.

Lévi-Strauss, C. (1996). *The Story of Lynx.*
Chicago: University of Chicago Press.

Liebling, A.J. (1956). *The Sweet Science.* New York:
Grove/Black Cat.

Linton, D. (2010). *Cloud Charts. Trading success
with the Ichimoku technique.* London:
UpdataPlc.

Livio, M. (2003). *The Golden Ratio: The Story of
PHI, the World's Most Astonishing Number.*
New York: Broadway Books.

Lorber, J. (1994). *Paradoxes of Gender.* New Haven & London: Yale University Press.

Lovelock, J. (2000). *Gaia, A New Look at Life on Earth.* Oxford: Oxford Paperbacks.

Lynch, P. (2000). *One Up on Wall Street.* New York: Simon & Schuster.

Mackay, C. (1841). *Extraordinary Popular Delusions and the Madness of Crowds.* London: Richard Bentley.

Malthus, T. (1983). *An Essay on the Principle of Population.* London: Penguin Classics.

Marx, K. (1992). *Capital.* London: Penguin Classics.

Maslow, A. (1997). *Motivation and Personality.* New York: Harpers & Brothers.

Maté, G. (2000). *Scattered Minds: A New Look at the Origins and Healing of Attention Deficit Disorder.* Toronto: Vintage Canada.

Mead, M. (2001). *Coming of Age in Samoa: A Psychological Study of Primitive Youth for Western Civilization.* New York: William Morrow Paperbacks.

Mead, M. (2001). *Sex and Temperament in Three Primitive Societies.* New York: Harper Perennial.

Mehrabian, A. (1972). *Nonverbal Communication.* Berlin: Walter De Gruyter Inc.

Mehrabian, A. (1972). *Silent Messages: Implicit Communication of Emotions and Attitudes.* Belmont: Wadsworth Publishing Company.

Mehrabian, A. (1980). *Public Places and Private Spaces: The Psychology of Work, Play and Living Environments.* New York: Basic Books.

Mentzer, M. (2002). *High Intensity Training.* New York: McGraw-Hill.

Morgan, D. (2001). *The Best Guide to Eastern Philosophy and Religion.* London: St. Martin's Griffin.

Munenori, Y. (2003). *The Way of the Living Sword.* Bloomington: iUniverse.

Murphy, J. (1999). *Technical Analysis of the Financial Markets.* New York: New York Institute of Finance.

Musashi, M. (1982). *The book of Five Rings.* New York: The Overlook Press.

Nerburn, K. (1999). *The Wisdom of the Native Americans.* Novato: New World Library.

Nietzsche, F. (1999). *Thus Spake Zarathustra.* Mineola: Dover Publications.

Oestermann Van Essen, M. (2013). *The Buddhist Trader.* CreateSpace Independent Publishing Platform.

Orwell, G. (1961).*1984.* New York: Signet Classic.

Patel, M. (2010). *Trading with Ichimoku Clouds: The Essential Guide to Ichimoku Kinko Hyo Technical Analysis.* Hoboken: Wiley.

Patterson, F. (1974). *Inside Boxing.* Washington: Henry Regnery.

Pavlov, I.P. (1984). *Conditioned Reflexes of the Physiological Activity of the Cerebral Cortex.* Mineola: Dover Publications.

Plato. (1925). *Statesman – Philebus – Ion.* Cambridge: Harvard University Press.

Plato. (1955). *The Republic.* London: Penguin Classics.

Plato. (1970). *Protagoras and Meno.* London: Penguin Classics.

Plato. (1970). *Laws.* London: Penguin Classics.

Plummer, T. (2013). *The law of vibration.* Hampshire: Harriman House.

Pring, M. (1995). *Investment Psychology Explained.* Hoboken: Wiley.

Pring, M. (2008). *Trading Systems Explained.* Colombia: Marketplace Books.

Pythagoras. (2007). *The Golden Verses and other Pythagorean Fragments.* Charleston: Forgotten Books.

Radhakrishnan, S. (2007). *Eastern Religions and Western Thoughts.* Oxford: Oxford University Press.

Rinpoche, S. (1904). *The Tibetan Book of Living and Dying.* San Francisco: HarperSanFrancisco.

Robinson, D. (1995). *An Intellectual history of Psychology.* Madison: The University of Wisconsin Press.

Rousseau, J.J. (1953). *Confessions.* London: Penguin Classics.

Rousseau, J.J. (1968). *The Social Contract.* London: Penguin Classics.

Rousseau, J.J. (1980). *Reveries of the Solitary Walker.* London: Penguin Classics.

Rousseau, J.J. (1985). *Discourse on Inequality.* London: Penguin Classics.

Saint-Exupéry, A. (1942). *Flight to Arras.* New York: Reynal & Hitchcock.

Saint-Exupéry, A. (1951). *Citadelle.* Paris: Nrf Gallimard.

Saint-Exupéry, A. (1974). *Night Flight.* New York: Mariner Books.

Saint-Exupéry, A. (1991). *The Little Prince.* Hampshire: Egmont Books Ltd.

Saint-Exupéry, A. (2002). *Wind, Sand and Stars.* San Diego: Harcourt.

Sambhava, P. (1993). *The Tibetan Book of the Dead: The Great Book of Natural Liberation Through Understanding in the Between.* New York: Bantam Books, Inc.

Schwarzenegger, A. (1987). *The Encyclopedia of Modern Bodybuilding.* New York: Simon & Schuster.

Smith, A. (2003). *The Wealth of Nations.* New York: Bantam Classics.

Spinoza, B. (1992). *Ethics.* Indianapolis: Hackett Publishing Company.

Taylor, T. (1986). *Life of Pythagoras.* Rochester: Inner Traditions.

Thoreau, H.D. (1995). *Walden: Or, Life in the Woods.* Mineola: Dover Publications.

Three Initiates. (1940). *The Kybalion: Hermetic Philosophy.* Chicago: Yogi Publication Society.

Tse, L. (1997). *Tao Te Ching.* New York: Vintage.

Tzu, S. (1994). *The Art of War.* Boulder: Westview Press.

Voltaire. (1978). *Zadig and L'Ingénu.* London: Penguin Classics.

Voltaire. (1991). *Candide.* Mineola: Dover Publications.

Voltaire. (2007). *Philosophical Letters.* Indianapolis: Hackett Publishing Company.

Voltaire. (2008). *Letters on England.* Sioux Falls: NuVision Publications.

Voltaire. (2010). *God and Human Beings.* Amhurst: Prometheus Books.

Von Clausewitz, C. (1989). *On War.* Princeton: Princeton University Press.

Watson, B. (1993). *The Lotus Sutra.* New York: Columbia University Press.

Weider, J. (1988). *Weider Bodybuilding System.* Boca Raton: Weider Publications.

Yalom, I. (1993). *When Nietzsche Wept.* Melbourne: Penguin Books Australia.

Yalom, I. (1997). *Lying on the Couch.* New York: HarperPerennial.

Yalom, I. (2007). *The Schopenhauer Cure.* New York: HarperPerennial.

About the Author

Mario Kfoury is a private investor with credentials in martial arts, physical education, real estate, aviation and Technical Analysis. Self-taught in the streets of Beirut, Brussels, London, LA and New York, he synthesizes his views on life through different disciplinary and cultural prisms in favor of a peaceful/secular agnostic Deism. The story he shares appeals for democratic-socialism founded on sensible educational and healthcare systems, rigorous tax regulations; and cautions against the perils of religious beliefs, demography, and the reckless attitude towards the planet and its ecology.